praise for S‹

'Something truly special.' – *GoodReads*

'A validating read for all.' – *Amazon Reviews*

'Thorough, informative and inclusive.' – Claire Estelle

'Written and curated with great care.' – *Dimity Hubbub*

'A wealth of human experience.' – Heather Parry

'EVERYONE needs to read it.' – Melisa Korkut

'It covers SO many things! So many different experiences.'
– *My Endometriosis Journey*, YouTube

'I didn't know how essential this book was until I started it.'
– Sarah Parkin

'Packed with heart … there's so much to traverse from [the]
personal to institutional.' – *The Skinny*

'I don't think I've come across such a comprehensive book of
essays before.' – *GoodReads*

'For so long, calling someone hormonal has been seen as a gendered insult. It's time to break the stigma and redefine it.'
– *IMAGE Magazine*

'I was so intrigued by the anthology's contributors and their
focuses – endometriosis, transition, trans pregnancy and
childbirth, male infertility, and the racialisation of reproductive
healthcare.' – *BookRiot*

'Whether it's through politically thoughtful pieces such as Sowemino's [essay] or Hudson's personal account of hormone therapy, *So Hormonal* is a publication with an agenda.'
– *Disability Arts Online*

'Essential reading for people like me who cannot know what it's like, but are ready to empathise.' – *Tamsin Writing Blog*

'The stories in this book demonstrate how it is still possible to define yourself in a world where people are so ready and willing to make that definition for you.' – Fiona Buckley

'These eye-opening accounts will implore you to question your relationship with your own body and its hunger for your appreciation.' – *The Irish Independent*

'Expect pieces that celebrate the wonders and joys of hormones, while also challenging the stigma and discrimination routinely faced at the intersection of hormonal experiences.' – *BooksfromScotland.com*

'When we hear of hormones, we may immediately think of cis women's experiences … [but] Monstrous Regiment [Publishing] does really diverse anthologies … and how it turned out was very different.' – *The Selkie*

'*So Hormonal* invites the public to think about how interactions with hormones intersect with social and political issues that exist in society.' – M. Sunnia, *Disability Arts*

'I've read a lot of personal writing on hormones, but this is the most comprehensive on hormonal experiences that I have come across … It is deeply refreshing to find stories about hormones from cis men, next to essays about hormonal joy, fertility, pain, neurodiversity, osteoporosis, Addison's disease, PMDD and so much more. The book represents "the hormonal experience" for what it really is: bodies in flux, also known as being human.'
– *Fictitiously Hillary*

So Hormonal

First published in the UK in 2020 by
Monstrous Regiment Publishing Ltd.,
Edinburgh, Scotland
editor@monstrous-regiment.com
www.monstrous-regiment.com

Distributed in the UK by
Monstrous Regiment Publishing Ltd.

Cover design by Emily Horgan
Typesetting by Hannah Killoh

ISBN: 978-1-9161179-3-8

Printed and bound in Scotland by Allander Print, Edinburgh

A COLLECTION
OF ESSAYS ON
HORMONES

So
Hor
monal

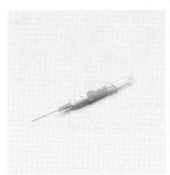

Foreword by Karen Havelin

Edited by Emily Horgan & Zachary Dickson

editor's note

I'M GOING TO keep this brief, as the words that follow these pages speak more powerfully than I could ever write.

Those of you who have experienced issues with hormones will know that the content in *So Hormonal* is not a new conversation. We find places to discuss these things – whether it's under anonymous usernames postfixed with numbers on forums, in covens of support groups, in riddles with our loved ones. But so often, these discussions are hushed away where others might not be able to find them. We are here to speak of them loudly.

This anthology was crowdfunded through Kickstarter at the cusp of a global pandemic. 333 people contributed to its creation by believing in the project and recognising the importance of the topics covered in this book. So much so, they put their money towards it. To those, we want to thank you.

Some guidance on reading this anthology – listen. Be uncomfortable, resonate, and reflect. There may be essays that you relate to, and some that you do not. That is okay. We have added a section to each piece with suggestions for what you can do next. If you are moved by what you read, action it. Read more and expose yourself to the realities of what folks experience and live with every day due to hormones.

Some of the pieces touch on the difficult realities of hormonal experiences – this includes medication, mental health difficulties, abuse, and grief. As editors, we have supported our authors to speak as openly as they feel comfortable with about these topics and have included trigger warnings where deemed necessary. If you resonate with some of the struggles that are outlined in these stories, our thoughts are with you and we hope you are receiving the care and support you need. You deserve to be looked after.

If you do not see yourself in these pages, please do not feel unseen. We see you. Experiences with hormones are unique in a way that cannot be described. Our book is just a glimpse, and cannot and would never claim to cover all experiences. The intersection is what makes these things so messy and beautiful. If you do not see yourself in this book, please reach out. We want to hear from you. We have moved these conversations to a public and permanent forum. We want you to continue them.

– Emily Horgan
July 2020

contents

please note

We would like to alert readers that some essays contain potentially triggering content, including discussions of mental health issues such as depression, PMDD, and body image disorders, and mentions of suicidal ideation. Additionally, these experiences are personal to each writer, and are not to be taken in the place of professional healthcare.

The following essays include discussions of:

foreword

by Karen Havelin

IT IS HARD to truly convey how much an altered cocktail of hormones can affect how you exist in the world. At times in my own life, I have wondered what core there is to me, or to anyone, considering how much hormones can change us.

When my hormones shift, I can feel strangely liminal. It sometimes feels like I hear music more intensely, as if it is inside my body. My sense of smell is stronger, and even more emotionally charged than normal. It sometimes feels like I can smell a big change in the wind. I can catch the scent of a stranger's perfume on the tram and suddenly feel like I *know* them. It can seem like I'm not sealed up enough against the world, or against other people.

I know I share the experience with many menstruating people of suddenly feeling weirdly heartbroken and angry, of wanting to burn everything to the ground over relatively minor provocations. That feeling of: *oh shit, I guess I'll have to get divorced, leave my job, and escape into the woods to live as a bog hag.* Then realising a hormonal event was on the horizon. *Oh, right!* I touch on this in the opening line of my novel *Please Read This Leaflet Carefully*: 'For years, I've considered it an established fact that the female body is a pain in the ass'.

The novel follows my main character backwards through time, from her post-pregnancy body on hormonal birth control at 35 at the start of the novel, through hormonal shifts due to endometriosis, from medically induced menopause tempered with different addback hormones, through untreated endometriosis wreaking havoc, to her as a 14-year-old figure skater in the throes of puberty at the end of the novel.

The ebb and flow of reproductive hormones washes over so many for most of their lives. But hormones are not exclusive to women in their reproductive years. The rest of us, too are ruled by shifts in tides that we often do not know about. We tend to associate hormones with only one gender and think of them as 'things that make women go mad', as Donna Alexander recounts her parents explaining it in her essay. Hormones can influence our identities, regulate our appetites, protect us when we are injured, turn us on or off. The much wider spectrum of how hormones influence us is what this anthology explores.

Reading this anthology was emotional for me. I have personal experiences with an unlikely amount of the themes. Like Laura, the main character of *Please Read This Leaflet Carefully*, I have severe endometriosis and have tried all manner of medically induced hormonal changes to get it under control. I also have secondary adrenal insufficiency, which means I have to take cortisone to live because my body doesn't produce the stress hormone, cortisol. The fine balance of hormones changes throughout the day in the human body, and trying to recreate that fine symphony with medication feels very heavy-handed. I've looked for a perfect metaphor for these medical attempts to recreate the hormonal harmony in the body. It could be something like trying to play the piano with thick winter mittens on. Trying to carve a roast chicken with a spade. Like heating a whole house with one electric panel heater. Parts of the house will be cold and parts will be scorched, no matter what you do. You can eat that bird, but it doesn't quite look like a party for humans anymore. There are soundwaves but they aren't likely to make you lean back in your chair, close your eyes and go 'ahhh'. (Of course, I would agree that it is a small price to pay to remain alive.)

This anthology has many intense moments, both of pleasure and pain. From Madeleine Dunne's desperate desire to be alive in her piece about puberty bringing childhood sexual abuse to the surface – to Alice Tarbuck's piece about the sometimes delicious and transcendent mystery of hormones she experiences: 'I let my body take me where it wants to, as far as possible – I try to make my body a good place to be in, for those periods of hyper awareness'. There is James Hudson's gorgeous essay about starting and stopping testosterone, and the difficulty of identifying who you are doing something for. There is also the delightful and candid essay about unexpected lust during menopause by Lins Ringer.

This anthology additionally presents more academic pieces, such as Heather Parry's exploration of the changes in personality due to hormonal changes with the help of Jean-Paul Sartre's *Nausea*, and further explorations of what people know and don't know about gender, autism, illness and health, and the simplistic views people often have of hormones and their effects. The very centre of it for me is right here, from the essay entitled 'Telling Hormonal Stories': 'it's hard to distinguish between what's "biological" and what's "social" in the way these stories play out'.

Having read the essays, I am tempted to think perhaps the divide between a person and their chemical components is somewhat artificial. Everything in our bodies and minds is connected, just as we are all connected to each other. Perhaps the shifts are the human experience, not some sort of exception or aberration. Maybe all these changes mean being a little bit permeable, and perhaps that can be an entrance to empathy. In the year since my own novel came out, I have realised that as rare as my particular situation is, there are a lot of people with equally rare health cocktails out there.

In some ways, we are our bodies, after all. We never know how long anything will last, least of all our health. The houses of our human bodies are built on shifting sands. Getting used to the surf is perhaps not such a bad thing.

no country for neurodivergent women

by Donna Alexander

I'M A NEURODIVERGENT clusterhead, and that's not a tongue twister. I live with Attention Deficit Hyperactivity Disorder (ADHD) and Cluster Headaches (CH). Popular opinion is that these are male disorders. When most people consider ADHD, they imagine little boys causing trouble, climbing the walls, shouting and hyperactive. This is outdated, and untrue. ADHD is a neurochemical disorder that impacts activity, attention, and impulsivity in children and adults of all genders in severe and chronic ways (Solden 23–24). It's an equal-opportunity disorder, but its impact differs case-by-case depending on gender, class, available support systems, and so on. Girls often mask their symptoms and may exhibit fewer hyperactive traits, instead fading into the background, withdrawn and inattentive.

In my experience, most people have never heard of CH. Those who know of it will likely think that CH affects men and migraines affect women. Statistically, more men are diagnosed with CH. But – and I preface this with the statement that I am not a medical professional – considering that it is well-documented that women's pain is not taken as seriously as men's, I would hazard a guess that there are plenty of women suffering in silence. CH is a neurological disorder that causes excruciating pain on one side of the head and/or face. CH attacks occur in clusters or cycles at least once every other day for a few weeks to a few months, and individual attacks last anywhere between 15 and 180 minutes. Excruciating pain is accompanied by restlessness, and autonomic symptoms such as facial flushing, runny nose, tearing, and swelling on the affected side of the head. The pain is so extreme that medical professionals have nicknamed CH 'suicide headaches'.

Delayed diagnosis

I was not diagnosed with either of these until recently due to societal, hormonal, and gender prejudice. Aged 31, a 'headache' so horrific that I considered ways to knock myself unconscious led to a CH diagnosis. I spent more times than I can remember clawing at my face and head, trying to pulverise pain that defies description. Following 13 years of misdiagnoses, and my parents' insistence that I was over-dramatic, I had a name for pain so bad I even wondered if I was imagining it. I put my diagnosis down to the pure luck of encountering an A&E doctor who knew about CH.

Arguably, the most effective treatment for aborting CH attacks is high-flow 100% oxygen hyperventilated via a non-rebreather mask, and triptans delivered via injection or nasal spray. These are my main go-tos. Other promising treatments are hormone-based or hormone-altering, such as melatonin and steroid tapers, and beta-blockers which block the effects of epinephrine. Research into hormones and CH is sparse, and little is understood about why some treatments work for some patients and not for others. But the effectiveness of hormone-based treatments surely merits further exploration. I recently searched threads in an online CH support group, and found that the notion of a hormonal connection was often dismissed as irrelevant because of the predominance of CH in men. These comments were scattered between hundreds of posts about common patterns of deficiencies or surpluses of hormones in blood panels. People seem to forget that men also have hormones coursing through their bodies, dictating emotions, regulating or disrupting neurobiological functions. This hormonal prejudice not only stands in the way of women's diagnoses, but our deeper understanding of the disorder.

ADHD, being a neurological issue, is also shaped by hormones, namely low levels of dopamine and norepinephrine. Guess which hormone impacts these? Oestrogen! These hormonal connections are only becoming more widely known and understood after decades of excluding women and girls from research. Oestrogen surges when we hit puberty, so it makes sense that girls tend to notice fluctuations of ADHD issues in their teens, around the same time that boys may notice their ADHD issues dissipating. I, like many teenage girls, had my issues dismissed as puberty, told that my hormones were 'at' me, and I was being a 'difficult girl'.

I was diagnosed with ADHD recently. After nearly two years of SSRIs and therapy for clinical depression, the majority of symptoms were under control. However, my distractibility, poor concentration, disorganisation, hyperfocusing, and impulsivity remained.* My diagnosis was relatively late, but not as late as some. Gabór Maté, physician and expert in childhood development and trauma, writes about the oldest person he ever prescribed Ritalin to – an 85-year-old woman 'who, on taking Ritalin, was able to sit still more than fifteen minutes for the very first time in her life' (p.16). I have not tried medication yet, but considering that I fall asleep rubbing my feet together and pulling my hair, I won't rule it out (and the person trying to sleep next to me every night certainly thinks it's a good idea!). The ADHD diagnosis painted the entirety of my life experiences with a new palette. Suddenly, all that was annoying and apparently unlikeable about me, all the splatters, splotches, and mess on the canvas had names. I started to find meaning and worth in the abstract.

One of my earliest ADHD memories is of a pair of lion statues in the village square where I grew up. Walking home from school one day with my mother, my school friend, and

---

* *Individually, some of these issues have been associated with past traumas. But when considered together, and measured in terms of frequency and impact on my quality of life, it's a clear case of ADHD.*

her mother, we passed these as usual. Our mothers stopped to have a few words before they parted ways. My friend and I climbed on the lions as part of some safari game. Then everything went blank. I lost time, several minutes at a guess. My friend and her mother had departed, and so had mine. I spotted Mom across the square, only about 60 feet or so away from me. Due to the skewed perspective of childhood, it looked like she was unreachable. My kneecaps stung as I clattered across the square shouting for her to wait. My distress was met with irritation, a common response throughout my life to what was deemed my oversensitivity. The same annoyance was applied to my health issues.

I began to understand the mood swings, and sensitivity that led to a corner of the living room being dubbed 'the wailing wall' because when I was a little girl, I often crawled behind the armchair and hid there to cry, sulk, or just be alone. Sometimes, my parents would hear little snores coming from that corner and find me fast asleep. The tight space that only had room for me was a cradle in the absence of comfort, and a shield from the eye rolls, frustration, and annoyance that I found overwhelming. I wanted to be alone often from a young age. I enjoyed my own company, and found groups distracting and overwhelming. Group play stressed me out because it seemed to take me longer than everyone else to grasp the rules of a game, or complete a sequence of steps in the correct order. I was embarrassed by what I thought was stupidity.

Whenever someone would try to coax me out from behind the chair, one of my parents would often say something to the effect of 'Don't mind her. Her hormones are at her'. This entrenched the idea that my hormones were to blame for everything that made me feel weak, misunderstood, and unlovable. I can't remember exactly what I imagined a hormone to be back then, but I remember my parents explaining them as things that 'make women go mad'. It seemed that these hormones were responsible for making me do the things that caused my mother to declare that she would 'get the nuns to come and take [me] away'. This may seem bizarre, but up until 1996 women in Ireland were still incarcerated in Magdalene laundries. So now we have a child who believes she is being controlled by some unknowable force called a hormone, is potentially insane, and may be kidnapped by nuns at her parents' request. Maté tells us that '[f]or a person with ADD, tuning out is an automatic brain activity that originated during the period of rapid brain development in infancy when there was emotional hurt combined with helplessness' (p.119). It's no wonder the unknowable planes of my brain were more welcoming than reality.

I remember our first family holiday abroad to Disneyland. One evening we went to the bar in the resort and some Disney characters arrived to dance with the kids. Every single child danced with Mickey Mouse while I wished for invisibility. My father looked at me with disgust and said, 'Why can't you just be normal like the other kids?' If I wasn't so afraid of his temper, my response would have been a nine -year-old's version of, 'Because I don't have the attention span to learn something when it doesn't interest me, because

I have overwhelming anxiety attached to failure due to the constant reminders that I don't fit into socially-constructed roles of girlhood and womanhood'. But in the moment, I just absorbed the shame, and it pickled inside me.

These are mild examples of the emotional hurt I experienced due to my, then undiagnosed, neurodivergence. If I were to try to determine the exact moment, or the worst culprits that left emotional scars big enough to compel me to zone out of my own life for seconds, minutes, or hours at a time, it would be like trying to isolate and classify every colour and brushstroke of a Jackson Pollock painting while blindfolded. I could touch the textures of the scatterings on the canvas, try to recall his work, yet ultimately become overwhelmed and overwrought, more traits of ADHD. But I can, as I pick over the abstract textures of memory, finger a few drips, splashes, and scratches that contributed to delays in the diagnoses of these issues.

No country for neurodivergent women

Enshrined in Ireland's Constitution is Article 41.2 which states that 'by her life within the home, woman gives to the State a support without which the common good cannot be achieved' and that the State will 'ensure that mothers shall not be obliged by economic necessity to engage in labour to the neglect of their duties in the home'. These words copper-fasten a collusion between Church and State to control the lives of girls and women, and they have been exploited to their most depraved possibilities. They may as well have written

'A woman should be a maid in the living room, a cook in the kitchen, and a whore in the bedroom'. Women in Ireland have, at one point or another, been denied divorce, property ownership, the right to work, protection from marital rape, reproductive choice and broader forms of equal healthcare, and other markers of equal citizenship in a civilised society. While we defeated many of these barbaric experiments in psychotic, evangelical patriarchy, some still persist.

Ireland is no country for neurodivergent women. We can be mothers and homemakers if we want to, even brilliant ones, but not without grappling with the challenges of chronic and severe pain, distraction, impulsivity, and disorganisation. Rather than the holy trinity of maid, cook, and whore, I would have to say that I embody the unholy chaos of a mess in the living room, a mess in the kitchen, and well, a hot mess in the bedroom! Considering that I routinely forget basic things like putting on pants, the thought of being an organised soccer mom who collects the kids on time and remembers to wash their sports kits before the big game is beyond me. The idea of rustling up a nutritious family meal while buckling under the horrific pain of a CH attack would be laughable if it weren't so damn sad to think of all the time pain steals from me. My kitchen floor festers while an unused mop stands against the wall, because whenever I decide to do a spot of cleaning, I get as far as filling the bucket, then I will decide to rearrange my bookshelves. Then I read a few passages from a book I forgot I had. Then I make coffee, then a coffee cake. Then I take a shower. Then I realise I only shaved one leg as I put on a pair of odd socks. Then, then, then. If I chose to buy into the myth of what my hormonal make-up and gender dictates my life to be, I truly believe the conflict between the myth and my reality would kill me.

Oddly enough, my ADHD and CH seem to complement each other. While both rob my time due to pain and distractibility, the hyperfocus that ADHD causes allows me to win back some time lost to CH cycles. Because of ADHD, I have no patience for small talk, and I am incapable of giving my time and energy to things that I have no interest in. In the periods between CH cycles, my time is never wasted, because, contrary to stereotypes, ADHD-ers are not time wasters when we find our passions. Luckily for me, some of the things my neurodivergent brain deems important enough for my hyperfocus are literature, TV, and feminism. While ADHD is misunderstood as a disorder that causes stupidity, underachievement, and repeated failure, those of us who live with it know that when something is interesting enough, it will steer our neurotransmitters in a productive direction. My interests led me to examine the representation of women in pop culture. Even before my diagnoses gave me a clinical understanding of myself, I identified connections with characters in books and on screens.

Monica's (messy) closet

There's a scene in *Friends* where perpetually pristine Monica's dirty secret is revealed. Her neurotic and obsessive attention to detail, neatness, and cleanliness comes unravelled when

Chandler opens her closet door and finds an incomprehensible mess. Sari Solden says that 'Women with AD/HD often live in a secret world. Some people call it passing for normal. [I] call it being locked in a [messy] closet' (p.41). In the eighth season, Monica's closet is a punchline to a long-running joke about the character. The inner chaos she fought so hard to contain is revealed. Many of Monica's neuroses are connected to her relationship with her parents, and their palpable disappointment in her. Pair this with her history of disordered eating, and she is a prime candidate for an ADHD diagnosis. Like Monica, ADHD women run the risk of burnout with the daily business of conforming to socio-cultural demands of womanhood. We can harbour shame and self-loathing when we do not meet those standards. We often stuff down our feelings, and push against the grain of our neurobiological inner-workings.

An ADHD-er in women's clothing

In *Mrs Doubtfire*, we see a man disguising himself within his idea of traditional womanhood in order to overcome his neurobiology. Daniel, married father of three, is a textbook example of male ADHD. His impulsivity means he cannot hold down a job and is seen as a reckless father and husband, destroying his marriage. In a bid to remain in his children's lives, he masquerades as elderly nanny, Mrs Doubtfire, a caricature of modest, domestic femininity: an excellent housekeeper, a firm but maternal carer. Apparently, a good woman is also chaste, for she tells Sally Field's character,

Miranda, that 'once the father of your children is out of the picture, the only solution is total and lifelong celibacy'. However, much like Monica's closet, the inner chaos of Daniel is revealed when Mrs Doubtfire's mask literally slips.

How do you solve a problem like misogyny?

The one representation of ADHD womanhood that gave me hope before I even knew that women could have ADHD is Julie Andrews' Maria Von Trapp. The lyrics of 'Maria' which ask 'how do you solve a problem like Maria?' provide a pretty lucid description of ADHD. The nuns trill that Maria's 'always late for everything, except for every meal', and she's 'unpredictable as weather'. The pendulating nature of the ADHD brain is perfectly summarised as both gentle and wild. At any moment, my mood can switch from unbridled joy to deep sadness. My energy levels can shift from feeling positively Olympian to borderline comatose in a matter of seconds. Because of this, many women are misdiagnosed with mood disorders and mental illnesses like Borderline Personality Disorder and Bipolar Disorder. In *The Sound of Music*, Maria's erratic behaviour has escalated to the point where Mother Superior decides to send her to work outside of the convent. It's strange to feel so wholly represented by the character of a nun, having grown up in Ireland where nuns doubled up as jailers, torturers, and judges.

However, the movie nuns are a much kinder bunch. Despite Maria's challenges, Mother Superior sees persistence, kindness, and creativity. Indeed, the symphony of Maria's inner conflicts are externalised through her love for the harmonising 'sound of music'. The discord of ADHD's challenges and the medley of its unique gifts are abundant in Maria's self-affirming number, 'I Have Confidence', a lyrical pep talk for herself, switching tempo and pitch in time with the deviations of her unique neurology. Unlike Monica and Daniel, Maria is unapologetic about who she is. Rather than sacrificing or stifling herself to fit in, those around Maria realise that they need to embrace some of her habits and mannerisms.

Instead of asking how to solve a problem like Maria, a more productive question would be 'how do we solve a problem like misogyny?' In Ireland, there was a tradition well into the twentieth century of entering a child into the priesthood or the convent. If you had both a nun and a priest in the family you were Catholic royalty! Many nuns were ordered into the convent after being deemed too wayward or wanton to do the family proud as a wife and mother. Indeed a nun who taught at the primary school I attended told us that her father put her into the nunnery because she had too many boys interested in her, and went on too many dates.

That same teacher saw something in me when I was ten years old because she wrote in my report card: 'She has a wonderful sense of humour, which comes to her aid! If her progress continues she will be very successful'. Pretty much every other report card describes me as messy, careless, distracted, and reliant on my sense of humour in sticky situations. I found that report card recently during one of my distracted meanderings through old boxes and folders. I don't know what compelled me to keep it at the time. But now it's in my desk drawer as a reminder to live by my mantra, *In a world full of Doubtfires, be a Maria.*

What next?

- **OUCH UK** (*ouchuk.org*) – Organisation for the Understanding of Cluster Headache raises general awareness of cluster headache and offers support and guidance to sufferers and their families.
- **ADDitude Magazine** (*additudemag.com*) – ADDitutde Magazine is a leading source of important news, expert advice, and judgement-free understanding for families and adults living with ADD.

the waiting room

by Hidden Ink Child

I SIT ANXIOUSLY in a waiting room. Surrounding me are chairs, pastel coloured walls, clean floors, a child smashing plastic toys onto a child-sized table, and a heavily pregnant mother looking somewhat exasperated trying to quietly persuade their child to stop making such a racket. And there are posters. Posters that read about fertility trials, about postnatal depression, about the importance of cervical screening, about having an IUD placed at the same time as delivering a child.

They're all aimed at women. Me and my uterus do not exist in this space.

My presence always feels charged here. It's not just the stress and sinking feeling combined with quiet anger that I'm never remembered in public health messages; I feel like I'm the only one, that I'm not supposed to be there at all. Both internal dysphoria cues telling me to leave, to get far far away, and a complete lack of representation around me in signage indicate the space *just isn't for me*.

I'm used to this now, but it stings almost as much as the actual physical pain of having endometriosis. I exist in a battle between my identity, my body, and the healthcare I receive.

The first time I had to attend a gynaecology appointment with a male gender presentation, I thought it would be okay. It was just a catch-up after having had a number of ovarian cysts rupture and needing to look at how to manage my endometriosis better. I was anxious and panicky, but tried to walk with confidence – just a dude, going for his gynaecologist appointment, no biggie…

My stomach twisted and my steps faltered as I read the sign at the hospital.

McNair Centre
(WOMEN'S HEALTH)

It could have been shouted in my face. It could have been a stab wound. It could have been a punch in the gut, the way it felt to read it. I felt sick. I stopped, and sat down on a bench, trying to take a second to gather myself. Trying to concentrate and remember that just because I had an appointment there, just because I had to access my healthcare in that space, didn't mean I was a woman. I'd spent 26 years looking inside myself to solve this identity puzzle. I was not wrong; the sign was wrong. It was hard not to take it literally – the sign felt like an invisible barrier, a force field repelling me away. I pushed on, got to the door, and I couldn't walk through. I started to weep, hyperventilating, trying to figure out how the fuck I was going to attend this appointment when I literally couldn't get through the door.

I wrote a note to the receptionist, delivered it, and left again, waiting outside, trying to gather myself. The nurse came out to meet me and gave me a hug, apologising, guiding me through the waiting room I knew well but which felt like a war zone, gendered language sniping holes in the very fibre of my being. Later, the nurse told me that they had to write 'Women's Health' because people kept getting lost. I felt like I had to lose a part of myself to attend.

Years later, for an unrelated reason, I went for a pelvic X-ray of my hip. By this time I was mostly and gratefully perceived as male in all interactions with others, including during more intimate healthcare settings. Sometimes this can require my own specific disclosure, alerting a professional to my having a different body composition than their expectation, and sometimes I don't see it as wholly necessary to disclose – for example, for an ear infection. As this pelvic X-ray was unrelated to anything gynaecological – they were looking for any abnormality in the bones in my hips – I didn't consider disclosing my trans-ness to be on the top of my priority list. As with many trans folk, I was happy to avoid the awkward conversations or possible intrusive questions that tend to follow such disclosure.

During the scan, I had to lie under the machine (moved into place by the technician) wearing only boxers, and I wasn't wearing a binder, so I thought it was pretty clear regardless that I wasn't cis. A self-conscious photoshoot of my bones later, the technician left the room to check that the image had been captured correctly. An unusually long wait ensued, and I was left in the empty radiography room debating whether I could go get my phone to take sneaky pictures of the cool machinery without risking discovery. When the technician finally returned, they asked rather tentatively, 'Are – Are you transgender?'

Only slightly perturbed, I replied that I was and queried the purpose of the question.

'Er, we, erm, just need you to sign this consent form to say there was no chance you were pregnant'.

Caught off guard by the request, and certain I was not pregnant, I laughed uncomfortably. 'Bit late for that now', I mumbled, and not wanting to make a scene or face a confrontation, I signed it hastily and made to leave. At the door, I turned and asked how they knew I was trans and was informed that my Mirena coil IUD showed up on an X-ray. I did amuse myself for a while wondering if there had been a gathering of rather confused technicians trying to understand how a Mirena coil could have ended up inside me before realising I could be a trans, not cis.

Needless to say, I processed the ramifications of the interaction later. What if I *had* been pregnant? What could have happened to the foetus? What if I didn't know the dangers of X-rays and pregnancy, and didn't think to disclose my trans status? I was left feeling uncared for and left out; an anomaly in a system clearly not designed for people like me.

Later, when asked to attend a bone density scan, the same problem came up on a section of an intake form labelled '*FOR WOMEN ONLY*' in bold letters. When I queried the criteria, explaining trans men should really be included, the radiographer sighed and explained that they'd had so many men angrily cross out questions, or answer them mockingly, they had felt the need to specify in such a way. Did the discomfort of insecure cis men justify my exclusion, I wondered? Did it fuck.

Some of the barriers I've faced are contrasted by the way in which my pain has been treated differently since transitioning. Last year, during a particularly horrendous pain flare, I remember repeated trips to the GP trying to ascertain the 'correct' circumstances to call an ambulance for severe pain. As I explained that I just really needed to know when it was okay to call unmanageable pain an emergency, my GP stared wide-eyed and said he was going to prescribe me stronger painkillers. My confusion at the time was genuine – I didn't have severe pain all the time, I just wanted to know when it was okay to call self-management impossible, rather than having to deal with the repeated episodes of foetal-position-crunched-on-the-floor-unable-to-move absolute abdominal agony. He reiterated that well, painkillers will help, and the mind-blowing statement that: 'Nobody needs to be in pain'.

Having lived a significant portion of my life managing chronic pain with variable severity, sometimes having led to vomiting and fainting, I consider myself a bit of a veteran of severe pain management. Usually I know it will pass and can manage. I had never before been to a GP who had told me that painkillers would be needed, and was keen to offer a solution to my pain. This was not the only time a GP would opt for managing the pain, and I have been prescribed pain relief much stronger than I had ever received prior to transition. I've considered at length the development of my self-advocacy skills, whether I have become better at communicating, whether I have found better doctors, whether medicine has developed in the last few years. One inescapable truth, however, is that now I present as male. A year before I transitioned, I had a serious internal haemorrhage from a ruptured ovarian cyst misdiagnosed as constipation in the hospital, with the additional insult of the doctor questioning my mental stability. Now, doctors just…believe me.

I can only conclude that I have been treated differently when in pain as a direct result of my change in gender expression. When I explain I'm in pain now, I am readily prescribed painkillers. When I give my thoughts on the causes of a problem, my opinions are generally respected and acknowledged. I don't believe this is simply because I have found better doctors; I fully understand it to be an inherent part of how people treat me now that I present and live as male.

Conversely, I have experienced exclusion as a result of my masculinity in spaces created to support patients. Early in transition, I realised how often Facebook endometriosis community groups had detailed 'No Men Allowed' in their guidelines. Not only were language and media around this disease exclusive, the entrance rules were, too. Although most groups only outlined such rules due to a lack of awareness or consideration of the needs of trans people, the effect was apparent; these communities couldn't see me, acknowledge me, or create any space for me, when prior to transition my presence was unquestioningly approved of and accepted. This naturally led to a sense of unease and anxiety about being present in physical community support spaces, which are still sporadic and volunteer-led. Would the lack of understanding around trans bodies and needs extend to these physical spaces? Would I be welcomed or shunned? Would I spend my entire time explaining myself, my existence, navigating that fine line between a benevolent educator, provision of free labour, and personal boundaries?

In reality, I have yet to test this anxiety in a physical community support group, but my assumptions were validated last year. During a thoroughly unpleasant experience with a consultant, I was told quite abruptly that I appeared too male to attend an NHS pelvic pain support group for patients with chronic gynaecological conditions. Although taking such discrimination to my MSP ultimately resolved the issue, it also appeared to come from a place of misunderstanding and judgement. In my engagement with endometriosis activists and patients, my peers have unanimously rallied behind inclusion and acceptance, once understanding that our experiences are more alike than different.

Ultimately, my body has become a battleground. My experiences are now an intersectional mess of feminist issues, trans issues, disability issues, and masculine privilege. This mix of privilege and persecution has been chaotic at best, isolating at worst. Overwhelmingly I am unable to simply access healthcare designed for my body; I routinely make a choice about disclosing my trans status when entering healthcare spaces. Accessing endometriosis-related care means I don't get the choice to disclose. I have to navigate spaces that are inappropriate to my needs as a whole person, anticipating the need to educate clinical staff and hoping that my navigation of these spaces leaves a clearer and less traumatic path for others like me. I am laid bare, my body an anomaly in a space that wasn't meant for me. Yet here I am, hoping that someday it won't be like this. Waiting for better. Fighting for better.

What next?

- **Every Month** (*everymonthcampaign.org*) – Every Month is a registered charity tackling period poverty across Greater Manchester. They create and distribute packs of menstrual products to food banks and other services for people living in poverty.

getting off the back foot with male fertility health

by Tyler Christie

I HAVE WANTED kids as long as I can remember. I don't know what it is, but I always saw having children as part of my destiny. It's not as if I had sentimental daydreams of family – rather it was a deep, subconscious expectation that kids were in my future.

Yet, throughout my twenties I was really scared of *actually* getting someone pregnant. Somehow I had been trained to think it would be so easy to get pregnant by accident and that it could happen at any time. I met my wife around the age of 30 and we dated for a number of years. She didn't want to use birth control as it tended to bring on big mood swings and migraine headaches for her, so the worry continued.

After getting married, we decided to try to conceive and actually, it happened just like that! We got pregnant quickly. I remember that the very day we found out, we also flew to meet my now-deceased grandfather and I finally introduced my wife to him. It was an amazing time and everything felt so easy.

Yet, five months later, my life was turned upside down. One night – the night before our first birthing class – my wife's water broke and we rushed to the hospital. A few days later, our daughter Mia passed.

It was the hardest thing I have ever been through and we grieved for months. About 12 months later, we got pregnant again and it felt like an eternity! But then eight weeks into the pregnancy, we had a miscarriage and lost our second baby. At that point I thought I would never have kids.

Realising I'm not alone

This is when I woke up. I realised that my dreams of having kids might not come true after all. I realised that fertility, unlike work or education, is something you can't just solve by trying harder. And I realised that getting pregnant and having a healthy pregnancy and newborn child are really hard for a lot of people. I was shocked that I didn't know this and that nobody had told me.

I learned that one in seven couples have difficulty conceiving,[1] that one in four pregnancies end in loss,[2] that nearly 50% of fertility difficulties are due to men,[3] that poor nutrition can significantly hinder fertility health,[4] and that mental health is correlated to preconception health and pregnancy outcomes.[5] I also experienced first-hand how few resources there are for men in this area and how, even for a not-so-macho guy like me, it can still feel taboo to talk about this struggle.

As I talked with more people, I found out that my experience was not unique at all. I saw that, like me, many people were delaying pregnancy until they were older. This is reflected in the data – more babies are now born to women over 35 than under 25 for the first time ever.[6] And I found out that the older you are, the higher the risk of complications.[7]

I kept thinking: why hadn't I learned all this stuff before? And why hadn't I had a plan for having kids, given it was so important for me in my life? The truth is the situation was a perfect recipe for depression. The feelings of self-blame, grief, and disappointment were constant. The accepted societal view that conception and pregnancy are 'easy' meant we were deeply unprepared for this difficult journey.

In the end we were 'lucky' and now have two daughters and a son. But I use 'lucky' in the way Oprah talks about it – that luck is 'preparation meeting opportunity'. We studied fertility health thoroughly, did blood tests to understand what might be holding us back, created a plan, implemented everything we could to improve our mental and physical health, and received support from amazing doctors. It was certainly a journey that tested our personal limits as well as the strength of our marriage.

I'm certainly not saying everyone should be worried or stressed about fertility or that there is a silver bullet formula for getting pregnant – sadly, many people will have unexplained infertility where there is no discernible cause. The causes of male infertility are complex.[8] However, with more awareness and better access to information, science, and support, people can take control of their journeys and create plans for their fertility that improves their chances of conceiving. And my hope is that the more people talk about it, the more it will help others on their journey.

That's exactly the focus of Parla, the company my wife and I set up after our own struggle in order to help others avoid the mistakes we made. At Parla, people can easily check in with their reproductive health through an online profile and at-home hormone tests, get expert-led guidance on how to improve mental and physical health, and connect with a community for support. A big part of our mission is to mainstream proactive health while breaking the taboos to empower people with the mindset to achieve their goals.

Men, it's time for action

While it's a broad generalisation, I feel most cisgender men are similar to me in that they don't really think that much about fertility. Then when they do, the default is to think about the female body. As a society, we predominantly think of fertility as a female issue and that success or failure rests on the women's shoulders. This could not be further from the truth, and it's time for men like me to step up.

There is good reason for men to take action – because we can! Most men produce millions of sperm each day. It takes the sperm about two and a half to three months to mature and be ready for game time. The cool part is that this resource of sperm regenerates every two to three months. Given the typical inclination of male egos (mine included!), we are pretty proud of this natural feat we accomplish.

Yet, the reality is that size is not everything in this department. The volume of sperm is just one factor, and the reality is that a lot of the sperm are never ready for game time. Think about it like all the sports players that never make it to the pros. For example, a large percentage of our sperm at any given time either doesn't know how to swim in the right direction to fertilise an egg or doesn't swim fast enough. So, before you get all psyched about the millions and millions of sperm on your team, you need to think about quality over quantity. Remember, it just takes one – do you want a Lebron James on your team or a bunch of amateurs?

This is totally different to women and people with ovaries who start with a certain number of eggs, called their ovarian reserve, which does not regenerate or increase over time. Of course, they can influence the health of their eggs and the other factors that contribute to fertility health. But the egg count is fixed. So, when couples think about fertility, it's important to tackle all the factors you can influence, and sperm health is a key one.

That's where the nuts come in (literally). Recent studies have shown that increasing antioxidant intake can help with sperm health. In couples where the cause of subfertility is a male factor (such as low sperm count), 30% to 80% of cases are thought to be due to the damaging effects of oxidative stress on sperm. In theory, this is when molecules containing reactive oxygen (called reactive oxygen species) overcome the semen's 'natural antioxidant defences' to cause cell damage. Increased levels of these molecules are thought to be due to several factors including pesticides, pollution, alcohol, smoking, and poor diet.

A recent study found that antioxidants can reduce oxidative damage.[9] The study found that couples where the men took oral antioxidants had a significant increase in live birth rate compared with couples where the men took a placebo. They also found that for couples where men took antioxidants, the couple had a significant increase in pregnancy rate.

As discussed in a study by Carlsen et al. (2001),[10] there's quite a range of nuts that can reduce oxidative damage. Walnuts contain huge amounts of antioxidants. Pecans, chestnuts, peanuts, pistachios, and sunflower seeds are also super rich in total antioxidants. Hazelnuts, almonds, Brazil nuts, macadamias, pine kernels, cashew nuts, flax seeds, poppy seeds, and sesame seeds can also help as they contain significant amounts of total antioxidants.

You can also take supplements to boost your antioxidants and increase other nutrients to help with sperm health. I personally took Proxeed, which is proven to improve sperm health in clinical trials, for three months before conception. There are many others out there as well – it's worth doing the research. Given the variety of factors that go into what makes sperm healthy and ready to fertilise, it's crucial to ensure all the key nutrients are covered in your supplements. So look for zinc, folic acid, vitamin B12, and Acetyl-L-carnitine, which can all help maintain sperm health and motility (the ability of sperm to swim properly).

Male infertility tests

This, I have to admit, was a bit of a weird one. Everyone is going to say 'Oh, it's so simple – get tested'. Well, that does depend. Just a few years ago when I took a test, it was in a basement clinic where an elderly nurse gave me a porno mag from the 1990s and an odd look, and then shuffled me to a back room. It was not the easiest experience, to say the least.

Yet, we all know that it's a lot easier to manage your health when you have clear information. So it's important to get sperm tested as early as possible. Whether you're already trying to conceive or not, you need to know where you stand. Luckily, it's now possible, including through Parla, to order a test online and do it at home – even with your partner – rather than in a strange basement.

If your sperm test results remain stubbornly poor, then it's time to explore some clinical help. A clinic will perform some more in-depth tests, such as a scrotaI ultrasound. A clinic may also explore hormone replacement or medications when infertility is caused by high or low levels of certain hormones. Even if these measures don't work, you'll also be able to explore assisted reproductive technology treatments. These methods essentially try to get the best sperm possible and insert them directly into the female genital tract, and/or use them in performing in vitro fertilisation or intracytoplasmic sperm injection.

To sum it up

To be blunt, don't be passive on this stuff, or you may have a similar experience to me and have your life turned upside down. You can take some simple steps to test your body, get smart about what's ahead and what you can do, and be a knowledgeable partner. You've got to pull your own weight on this one, because nobody else can.

And, importantly, go easy on yourself and your partner. This journey can be an emotional rollercoaster as our bodies, hormones, expectations, hopes, and fears evolve. The more you level up with your partner to be on the same page, become knowledgeable about your body, and grow aware of your emotions, the more prepared you'll be for whatever life throws at you.

What next?

- **Parla** *(myparla.com)* – Parla is changing the conversation around fertility from one that is often impersonal and fragmented to one that is accessible, holistic and empowering.

the self-made body

personal growth and steroids

by Michael Collins

Captain America is probably the world's most popular steroid user, if you think about it. An under-developed young man takes a super-soldier serum, becomes a paragon of physical strength, then goes off to punch Nazis. People don't think of him as a steroid user, of course – but why not?

Most people who take steroids don't have goals as noble as fighting fascism. The most prominent goal people associate with steroids is 'cheating at sports', but in reality that's only a small fraction of users. Most people who use steroids aren't athletes or superheroes. We – all kinds of people – use them to change how we look.

Is it purely a shallow desire? I've worn my muscles as armour, hoping they might deter any gay bashers who'd otherwise target me. I've physically put myself between a vulnerable person and an aggressive person, using my physique as a shield for the person being attacked. I've been a pretend boyfriend for friends who don't feel safe.

But those are secondary. I'm not a superhero, even though I took the super-soldier serum. I'm just a simple gay man who wants big muscles because it makes me happy. It turns me on. It brings me peace. It helps me be who I want to be. Are these shallow desires? I argue they aren't.

Premise: what if anabolic steroids are sometimes good?

Of course they are. They're medicine. Burn victims and people with degenerative diseases need them. Trans men need them. Cis men whose bodies don't make enough testosterone on their own, for whatever reason, need them. A doctor can write a prescription for all these people.

But steroids can also be an aesthetic tool for informed and consenting adults. This is classified as abuse, but I think that's oversimplifying matters. Many rational, good-willed people have researched the risks and decided steroids are an acceptable bargain for them, that they are a net benefit to their lives.

Perhaps you believe you've never met such a person. In that case: Hello. Here I am. You now know one.

This is the scariest essay I've written in my 13 years of being published because, well, steroid use comes with a lot of stigma. A lot of people are miseducated about them, but are confident in that faulty education. People might think I'm a cheater, even though I'm not involved in any sport that bans steroids – I'm cheating at life, at sex, and at gender. They might think I'm fatally enamoured with toxic masculinity. They might think I'm a ticking time-bomb roid-rager. They might think I'm a fetishist who's decided a heart attack at 40 is a worthwhile price to satisfy my hard-on.

If anyone reading this feels that way, I can only ask for your patience; that you read this with an open mind.

We who use steroids without a strict medical need are still, well, *people*. We are driven to do this out of a deep and persistent sense of need. No one does steroids on a whim. It's not a bump of coke you might impulsively accept when offered at a party. A first steroid cycle is a ten-to-12-week commitment to sticking a terrifyingly long needle into your ass every few days. It is a very deliberate and long-considered choice. Why would a reasonable, thinking, feeling person, a person with a sense of self-worth and family and friends who love them, do such a thing?

I hope I can explain a little.

There's only one genre of essay I know where people admit to steroid use: the cautionary tale. The ones where steroids are a seductive but ultimately destructive thing: a siren, but *super butch*. The person in question fell victim to their own insecurities, their own body dysmorphia, their own anxieties about not measuring up, about being unwanted, and they drank from that poison chalice – but they know better now! They regret that choice!

I don't regret my choice. I was not seduced. I was not weak when I made my decision – in fact, I had to overcome so much fear and negative societal attitudes that it was an act of strength and defiance, a bold moment of self-determination, when I began using steroids.

After I finish writing this draft, I am going to go to my bathroom. I am going to carefully fill a syringe with golden oil. I am going to swab my left butt cheek with alcohol, then I will push the needle into my glute. I will bury it to the hilt. I will empty its contents into that muscle. The oil is thick, it takes about 90 seconds for it all to go in. You have to push really hard. It doesn't hurt but it is uncomfortable. This will allow me to push myself harder during my workouts. It will allow me to recover from those workouts more quickly. Over weeks and months, my body will grow more muscle tissue than it otherwise would.

This isn't how it is all the time. Sometimes you take your foot off the accelerator, give your body a break. It's a dance between desire and practicality, a way to slowly push the envelope without screwing up your health. Slow step forward, pause. Slow step forward, pause. Do that for several years and one day you'll wake up inhabiting a nature-defying body that should not exist, a body you have carefully created. A self-made mutant, a techno-male, a hormonal cyborg.

All my life I felt something akin to dysphoria, a word I'm hesitant to use, but nothing else in my vocabulary suffices. Not a dysmorphia. A dysphoria – a feeling like my body wasn't how it was meant to be. And I don't mean the casual body fascism of the six-pack-ab brigade and the attendant traumas we have all felt. I don't want that. I wanted – I want

– to be abnormal. To be a monster. I want to be 300 pounds with paper-thin skin and bulging veins. I want normal people to think I'm disgusting. I want stares of disbelief when I walk in public.

Photos lie to us, mirrors lie to us. It's distressing to look at a photo taken at an unfortunate angle and see my tall slender frame. I look small there. And it's so wonderfully encouraging – thrilling – to look at another photo, different angle, different lighting, and see my body blossoming with excess size, the surfeit of meat that reshapes my form, makes me bulging and wide and *different looking* than normal people. I look big there.

I love it. It feels right. It gives me life.

Why am I wired this way? It goes back as long as I can remember. Muscles fascinated me. Bodybuilding magazines were my first porn; muscles are my primary sexual identity. For my teens and twenties, I hid this fact about myself. I was a blue-haired Tori Amos fanatic with a 4.0 GPA. I was a skinny unathletic bookworm. I was in the drama club.

Coming out wasn't so bad – people expected someone like me to be gay. But if they ever found out I wanted to be a bodybuilder, a freak, impractically huge? That nothing else excited me like that did? It was mortifying to consider. I'd suppress panic every time someone borrowed my computer, with its thousands of saved images of flexing bodybuilders tucked away in folders with misleading names. What if they saw something they shouldn't? At the bookstore, I'd guiltily leaf through bodybuilding magazines, my senses on high alert, greedily gulping down the forbidden images. If someone approached I'd hastily stuff it back and grab something more in character, *National Geographic* or *NME*.

My desires were a constant companion, and they terrorised me.

I eventually found the strength to be unashamed of who I am, to pursue what I want. I started seriously working towards becoming a bodybuilder when I was 30. Better late than never.

I didn't start using steroids then, though – that's important to stress. If you're smart, you'll wait a couple of years after starting the bodybuilding lifestyle before you consider steroids. You need to learn how to work out in a way that will grow muscle, and that takes time. You need to learn how to eat in a way that will grow muscle. You need to build a base of strength and competency in the gym. You need to establish a whole new lifestyle and make it routine.

You need to learn about steroids and become safely informed about a complex topic with a fair amount of science you have to absorb. You won't have the luxury of a medical expert to guide you, and the endocrine system is complex and important. The only person who can keep you safe is you. (NB: being candid with your doctor is the wisest thing; I am with mine, now. I get regular blood work to help make sure I'm healthy and to nip any potential problems in the bud. But this medical support is a luxury not everyone can access; not everyone can safely disclose steroid use to their physician.)

All of this learning, creating an entire new lifestyle and adhering to it long enough that it becomes a new normal – that takes years. After that, you can consider steroids.

But why take them at all? Why not just…lift harder, eat more? Some people think you can achieve a modern bodybuilder's physique with hard work and dedication alone, given enough time. You can't. It is simply impossible. It would be like thinking you can make your hair blue if you just concentrate hard enough. You've got to use chemicals because the body just doesn't do that on its own. There are natural biological limits, and these drugs allow you to exceed them.

I tend to think of steroids and bodybuilding as a form of body modification. Body modification inscribes the will onto the body. Refuting biology as destiny. Biology is powerful, yes, something to be negotiated with, reckoned with…but it is not destiny. The currents are strong, but technology has given us a pair of oars; we can steer the ship to some degree. Carefully, patiently, into new waters.

Muscles are sexual currency for a lot of gay men. They're gender-confirming for a lot of trans men. They're…let's call them gender-reassuring for a lot of cis men. Non-binary people want muscles. There are women who want muscles too. There are female bodybuilders who share my desire to far exceed the limits of what society deems appropriate and attractive, to rewrite biology to better reflect their own desires (why? I can't speak for them, and also, I can barely explain the 'why' of it myself, when it comes to my own desires). Point being: many people want muscles, for many reasons.

But muscles are really hard to grow! Muscle tissue is incredibly 'expensive', metabolically. Under ordinary circumstances, your body doesn't want to carry around more than it needs. To grow a significant quantity of muscle, you need to be strict about your diet. You need to work out really hard many times a week. You need to avoid alcohol. You need to go to bed early.

These aren't sacrifices most people are willing to make, but they still want the muscles. So people look for shortcuts. Some think steroids are a magic pill that will conjure muscles out of thin air. They don't conceive of them as an add-on to all that hard work. They think of them as a replacement, not a supplement.

Steroids aren't a magic pill. Steroids are like a power-up in a video game. If you don't know how to play the game, you won't capitalise on the power-up while it lasts. You might end up wasting it entirely. All the boring awful stuff people are hoping to avoid – strict diet, gruelling workouts, limited partying, lots of sleep – still need to be done, even if you're using steroids. Without that dedicated bodybuilding lifestyle in place, steroids will give underwhelming results – and they will be more likely to cause health problems.

Everyone knows steroids are dramatically bad for you, right? I've seen so many Instagram and YouTube comments on professional bodybuilders' accounts – anonymous internet jackals gleefully predicting the muscleman's imminent death because of steroid use.

Steroids are *not* safe. But the harm they do can be mitigated. A 2010 study published in *The Lancet* comparing a number of drugs on the basis of how harmful they are stated that steroids, while not harm*less*, are safer than marijuana and *significantly* safer than alcohol.[1]

Steroids don't dramatically alter a person's personality. The popular line among steroid users is that steroids will just take whatever your personality is and make it a little more so. If someone has pre-existing anger management issues, well, that little testosterone-aided boost of confidence probably won't help the situation. But steroids don't turn nice people into nasty people.

Steroids can cause blood pressure to increase. This can be countered with a healthy diet and cardiovascular exercise. The same goes for cholesterol – steroids have a negative impact on lipids, but this can be counteracted with lifestyle choices that a serious bodybuilder should be making anyway. This is one reason negative health outcomes are more common for people who take the 'magic pill' approach to steroids and use them without having a strong exercise regimen and healthy diet in place – the harmful effects of steroids are blunted by beneficial lifestyle choices, but they will compound harmful lifestyle choices.

So steroids aren't good for you. They're also not necessarily that awful for you, if used properly. If people knew more about them, and there wasn't such a stigma about their use, simple harm reduction measures would be a lot easier to put in place. There would be more happy, healthy muscleheads living with less shame, and more informed adults capable of making healthier decisions.

I don't regret steroids, and I intend to continue using them. They've improved my relationship with my own body. They've improved my mental health. They've helped me pursue desires and an identity that I once felt deeply ashamed of. They've given me a sense of agency over my physical form, and over my life.

I worry, though. What if my family finds this essay? My mother frequently warns me not to get any bigger – what would she say if she learned I was taking these villainous drugs in pursuit of just that goal?

People often criticise fitness professionals and Hollywood actors for their lack of transparency regarding steroid use. They argue that these juiced up media bodies give the false impression that all that ripped muscle derives solely from hard work and proper technique (both of which are also non-negotiable aspects of acquiring those bodies, I hope I've stressed). But – the price of honesty is so high. Possession of steroids is a felony in the United States, and they are illegal to some degree in most western countries. They are also deeply stigmatised. Even if someone feels they can admit to steroid use without legal peril, there is likely a high social cost to pay. Perhaps you'll lose your job. Perhaps your friends and family will think about you in new, negative ways.

This weighs on me. And yet, I want to be honest. Steroids have been a very positive thing in my life. Whatever harm they've done has been negligible, the benefits deep and meaningful. They have helped me. They've made me happier. They've made me more fulfilled. They've allowed me to change my body in ways I've long and deeply desired – to take possession of my own body, really.

I hope anyone who loves me won't think less of me for that.

What next?

- ***Testo Junkie: Sex, Drugs, and Biopolitics in the Pharmacopornographic Era*** by Paul B. Preciado
- ***Pleasure Consuming Medicine: The Queer Politics of Drugs*** by Kane Race
- **Drug Policy UK** (*drugpolicy.org*) – An American group that advocates for compassionate, evidence-based drug policies, including decriminalisation and destigmatisation.

notes from a medical menopause

there's a tea for that

by Alexia Pepper de Caires

menopause (n.)
'the final cessation of the monthly courses of women', 1852. From 1845 French *ménopause*, from medical Latin *menopausis*, from Greek *menos* for 'month' (from root *me- 'to measure') + *pausis* 'a cessation, a pause' from *pauein* 'to cause to cease'. Earlier it was *change of life* (1834).[1]

When did we lose 'change of life'?

Before

I LIVED QUITE happily with, and without the knowledge of, my cancer for several years. Maybe as many as seven.

Life wasn't perfect, of course – anxiety–depression cycles spiralled hard and fast, I dropped out of a salaried income and my body sent me regular warning signals. On balance though, it was functional.

The signalling ramped up in early 2019 by way of an infected appendix. During a short hospital visit I was treated to a dose of patronising by male consultants who smilingly suggested that my reluctance to leave without a diagnosis was because I had my own room. On release, I bought a comfier sofa and spent several months nestling into my new velvet cushions, waiting for scan appointments to plop through the letterbox. 'Scanxiety' is the brilliant term I later learnt for this.

But surely it couldn't be anything serious. I knew this as I'd gently probed an odd set of symptoms in 2017 once they formed a pattern and registered the alarm. With my brain set to alert for early onset menopause, which runs in my herstory, I had asked to be tested for being perimenopausal. 'Peri' as in 'near', 'menopausal' as in 'woman not to be believed'. The GP half-listened with a suspicious ear given my age, found nothing in my bloodstream, and suggested it was stress. With most sources of stress now cut out of my life as well as regular visits to a massage therapist who calmed my heightened adrenal response, this diagnosis didn't resonate. A prescription for SSRIs (antidepressants which help promote serotonin uptake in the brain to offset depression) was duly written and I went back to a chemical crutch for my struggling mental health. Prevention being better than cure doesn't extend to female health, as the cost of ignoring our needs is apparently nothing.

With more time in my life and on the advice of my mental health therapist, I had then sought out a homeopath to discover how else I could self-care. All these alternative therapists made my life manageable and ate into my financial savings. Stepping into this practice every few weeks to gently talk through my physical, emotional, and practical wellbeing with a kind soul was wonderful. I thrived on opening up without the five-minute stop watch and that oppressive GP opener 'So, what can I do for you?' (I always have to respond in my head 'Find out what's wrong and heal me is pretty standard, no?') My menstrual cycle went back to a reliable 28 days, the need to suddenly and urgently pee stopped and my mind eased. I mentally planned a few more years of camping holidays.

Back on my sofa in January 2019, it would take three months, a self-funded yet inconclusive MRI scan – because I never received that letter and wanted answers – followed by an inconclusive CT scan to finally get a call to see a new consultant in a few days' time. Which would be good, unless it was bad – I couldn't imagine that possibility and proudly resisted my anxious internal voice. I did spot that of the 11 consultants listed in the department, just one had a female name. Patriarchy in healthcare, thou art so enduringly strong.

Answers

My exhausted cells danced with sheer relief when I learned what the surgical team had in store for me. Major surgery for suspected colon cancer in two weeks' time! *Answers*! *A plan*! It was too surreal to take in, and as I was also knee-deep in grief for a parent figure, the strange words coming from the kind consultant's mouth floated around the room. Omentum. Hemicolectomy. Heated chemotherapy. Possible pseudomyxoma peritonei (that last concoction was my favourite).

There was a lovely nurse in the consulting room to support us. This was the best NHS experience I'd had in my adult life; I should have clocked it as epically life-changing too. My life partner did way before me, when the first questions asked were whether I had or wanted children. I was in linear mode. This was not connected to my painful abdomen.

Channelling my millennial Biological Sciences university degree, I found intellectual joy in discovering what lay ahead. The tumour would be identified and removed, along with my ovaries (oh, that's the link…), part of my small intestine, appendix, and omentum – a stretchy layer of fatty tissue protecting the abdomen. Piping hot chemo would be swashed about internally to kill off any sneaky cancer cells. I'd be lying open on the operating table for six to eight hours and in recovery for three to six months to gain the best chance of future health. There was no hesitation when I consented to this treatment plan. My body would all be better very soon. Simples.

Hold on – if you remove my ovaries, I'll go through the menopause when I wake up. Surely that's worth a quick chat about?

The kindly (male) consultant smiled at the lovely (female) nurse. 'Oh, I think they recommend a tea for that these days', he said, glancing at her for approval. 'Ask your GP'.

And with that, my medical menopause was reduced to a matter of such little importance that the consulting room hardly heard it. My anxious mind was already working hard to wrap itself around all the new phrases and concepts. There was no space for me to say that I'd been preparing myself for this change of life and knew it could really disrupt my wellbeing. They suspected cancer, and my emotions fell in line with the NHS' prioritisation.

For the next fortnight I had to work to suppress my feeling of revulsion when imagining the quiet, precise violence of men in clean white coats removing my vital organs, their chemicals keeping me still and unaware. My desire to live was so strong I could taste it, so I deployed all the cognitive dissonance I could muster and dug deep.

Every now and then I saw the word 'menopause' zoom across my brain, perhaps sent by my scared reproductive system. Ovaries waving from the open sea to shift my focus, however no lifeboats could be sent. My energy reserves were at an all-time low from illness and grieving.

Menopause isn't the word I really want to use. Nothing pauses, everything changes.

Not all the change is bad: I immediately delighted in the idea of giving up menstruation and all its micromanagement. Tired of the smells, mess, sharp mood shifts, intensified travel sickness, and sheer cost of it all. Even with the Clue app (a data tracking app used to predict periods) I was hardly ever prepared to deal with the hassle. I had begun to suspect that

PMDD (premenstrual dysphoric disorder) played a role in my more murderous PMT episodes, which thanks to medical misogyny I only discovered aged 41, a month before the cancer diagnosis.

Now I would be free from its grip. And thus would begin my elegant transformation into a wise owl, released from society's expectations of me as a fertile woman. I imagined myself with glossy grey hair and cheaper monthly living costs, no more guilt about whether or not to use moon cups.

The 'tea' response was still bothering me though – I don't really drink it and felt sceptical about its potential to support a complete change of my hormonal profile. Another thing that runs in my maternal bloodline is huge sensitivity to hormones, from migraines to polycystic ovaries via endometriosis. I thought I'd cross that bridge later.

Yet that bridge turned into a very long road.

Treatment

Surgery was a clear success and for a few months, recovery went well. I asked my GP about what could be done to support the lack of oestrogen in my weakened body. He needed to wait until we had the results confirming what sort of cancer I'd had before thinking about that; if it was hormonal, then HRT would be dangerous. I tried to settle into my newly reduced mobility and adopted a greyhound. Herbal remedies in place of state-funded treatment helped me feel like I was taking my full health needs seriously, and I swallowed this latest gender tax as gracefully as I could.

My monthly expenditure for a female body hadn't changed at all.

Our free healthcare system had amazingly removed a seven-centimetre stage two burst tumour from my appendix, a highly rare cancer type, and worked hard for hours to keep me alive. I know it was a tough operation as the anaesthetist came to see me on the ward, smiled to see me doing okay, and told me how well I'd done on the operating table. Yet after a week in hospital and a later course of chemo, the support was gone. The menopause remained invisible, like all those pesky hormones which see female lab rats systematically excluded from medical research and clinical trials.

Then I had a round of chemotherapy I was allergic to, requiring lots of steroids. My obliterated immune system led to several stubborn infections and many antibiotics. None of which my body liked very much, and so my thyroid stopped working.

Why was my skin ultra-sensitive to touch? Were the hot flushes post-chemo or menopausal? Which deficiency caused my heightened irritability? The trifecta of chemotherapy, menopause, and a broken thyroid could not be neatly separated, whatever the doctors wanted.

I didn't know where to start with the GP anymore, seeing a different locum every time. Nothing felt like it was helping. I'd been put on a new concoction of drugs to support my fragile mental health, but I could no longer cope with all the different tablets for different things. I stopped taking them all (which is never recommended by health professionals).

These now just looked at me from my bedside table:

- SSRIs to boost my fragile mental health
- Calcium + vitamin D to prevent menopause-induced reduced bone density
- Herbal menopause support to relieve the symptoms
- Probiotics to try to rebuild my intestinal microbiome which had been obliterated

My throat refused to swallow any more pills. My brain cells refused to learn any new words. My mind and body were overloaded and increasingly, dangerously detached from each other. I had a double dose of brain fog and struggled to know where to turn.

The GPs kept changing and admitted they were out of their depth. One wrote to the oncologist to check what cancer I'd had, as she couldn't find the right letter on my file. The backlog of patients was too long to get a reply. When I was sent for genetic cancer testing I spotted a specialist Women's Hospital in my home city, but no one referred me to it and I was too exhausted to ask.

My mental health was never reviewed in light of my menopausal adjustment, and no testing of my hormone profile was ever scheduled. The hospital forgot to book me in to see a nutritionist, and both physio and mental health needed me to self-refer. Difficult to access when you're exhausted by a walk to the kitchen.

Aftermath

The lowest point came during a break from my home to see my family, in a different city. The complexity of my health felt too hard and I couldn't see what could change. So, with no hormones to stimulate my thyroid to produce energy for my cells, no oestrogen and marginal testosterone, exhaustion and frustration led me to suicidal thoughts one night.

And then I looked over at my peacefully snoozing dog, and mercifully, one hormone surged. Oxytocin. I'm lucky I had people to go to for help later that night. I'm lucky they wanted the best for me and made sure I had company every minute from then to keep me safe.

What goes undiscussed in the UK's NHS is how closely the immune system, digestive system, reproductive system, and mental health are connected. My wonderfully talented massage therapist lent me a book written by an American doctor, who makes the case for female depression being a symptom, not a cause, of dysfunction in this endocrine system. No tablet can ever replace a proper examination of our full selves in all our natural complexity.

> The true cause of depression is not simply a chemical imbalance, but a lifestyle crisis that demands a reset. It is a signal that the interconnected systems in the body are out of balance – from blood sugar, to gut health, to thyroid function – and inflammation is at the root.[2]

The vacuum of interest in understanding my hormonal needs has struck me as the very definition of a patriarchal health system that was quick to wield the knife. In meme form – if you can't see them, are they even real? Hormones, like emotions, bear the weight of being too female-associated to warrant investment by our institutions of power.

When my thyroid kickstarted again, after waiting patiently on the advice of a private endocrinologist to understand what was happening there, I tried to research medical menopause online. All the guidance and information I found assumed that my loss of ovaries was from gynaecological treatment, and that my specialist team would be supervising. There wasn't a single source of support for someone going through menopause for a different reason, like non-ovarian cancer. My menopause was invisible to my cancer team, and my appendix cancer was invisible to my female healthcare needs.

No one should have their ovaries, or any part of their reproductive system, removed and be sent home without a plan of action. We need women's hospitals – and more of these – to join up with surgical services to support people before and after their surgery. Menopause brain fog reduces the tracking of information and processes to an excruciating crawl, so medical teams need to enable access to hormonal support ahead of the really hard work. This is what a modern, humane healthcare system looks like, not centring the disease but the full person.

I'm still on the bridge, which feels like a tightrope designed to test my emotional resilience. Yesterday, a letter arrived to cancel my appointment with the Women's Hospital due to the coronavirus pandemic. This specialist chat would have happened 13 months into my medical menopause.

Maybe I'll learn to drink tea instead. And as I slurp, think about all the men with impotence who are never offered a cuppa as a solution.

What next?

- **Cysters** (cysters.org) – Cysters is a grassroots charity, dedicated to supporting individuals and improving the health, education, and welfare of those with reproductive and mental health issues. They aim to educate the public about reproductive health and education so that they can make informed choices around their treatment options and challenge the cultural misogyny behind reproductive health.

'man...i feel like a woman'

experiences of a trans woman's oestrogen therapy to treat gender dysphoria

by Kacey de Groot

IMAGINE YOU DROP a really heavy thing straight onto your toe. It causes a break, is medically 'fixed', and six months later… the injury has completely disappeared. Like it was never there. If there is an advantage to dropping a really heavy thing onto your toe, it is this: you immediately know something is wrong, your body highlights that to you (and importantly, the people around you) with bruises and blood. Doctors are able to intervene at all stages of healing, ascertaining precisely what the problem is. With those around you 'seeing' your injury, they will understand something of your experience, visually at least. Hopefully, they will be kind. They might fetch things for you, not insist you undertake a four-mile walk to a beautiful beach, offer sympathy and understanding when pain levels are high.

Now imagine a pain that is the opposite of this. It starts very gradually and increases in minute increments. Day by day, you are unsure if that pain is better or worse than the previous day. Because there aren't any physical symptoms, this kind of pain can be quickly misinterpreted or dismissed as imagined, or psychosomatic. At the point in time when it has started to become all-encompassing, you visit a doctor. If there are physical and medical traces, the doctor, in all but the rarest case, won't be looking or testing for them because something different will be on his mind. (I chose the 'his' pronoun here with care.) The 'peaks and troughs' make you capable of having 'good days' which can convince those around you (and yourself) that there is nothing wrong with you. As the long process continues, those around you lose patience and sympathy more and more. You are not like your old self, you should try and exercise, you should cut down on drinking, you should have a top night out and get wasted, you should stop being selfish…and the list goes on.

For me, as a trans woman, the process of accepting that reality was long and drawn out. I just *couldn't even*. The feelings and symptoms I would now recognise as 'dysphoria' – although that 'recognising' is far from foolproof – were present from childhood. But I couldn't anchor them to anything as concrete as gender. My denial and fear in early childhood had locked my gender identity deep, deep inside of me. My puberty led to an escalation in my sense of self-unease and discomfort. Basically, and in a nutshell (sic), my testicles had started to swamp my body's systems with testosterone. I couldn't have explained that to anybody at the time, but the memory of that feeling is still vivid today.

I then accidentally connected to the notion of gender. Social construct or biological reality, it exerts vast power over all of us, and doesn't care if it's 'real' or not.

Swiping lipstick clumsily onto my teenaged lips changed my reflection enough that I gendered myself (for a moment) as female. This did connect me to aspects of my repressed childhood, but it also connected me to images of transvestitism and crossdressing. And in those days, while not the fault of the people who were lampooned, this was not a positive and empowering thing to aspire to. Arguably, it still isn't. So I did what I did best. I buried it deeper. My mum has recently recounted how she saw the change in me around that time. How life drained from me. How I retreated and closed down. And how she tried, failed, and then wished she could understand and help me. Sadly for us both, that wasn't to be for another 35 years. This is when the confusion about my own gender identity, and the physical reality of the pain of dysphoria, collided.

I have read about the lived experiences of trans young people who were able to connect the dots from very early in their lives. When a 'wrong puberty' starts, they are able to see and identify why their bodies are not right for them. I experienced the pain, but its hidden nature and unknown source enabled me to dismiss it. It was being a teenager, puberty, or just being a 'Holden Caulfield', surrounded by others who didn't seem like me.

For the trans young people who do know the source of their pain, the onset of puberty, which will bring horrendous body changes to them (contrary to their peers) must be unbearable. Imagining your daughter growing a beard and having a broken, deeper voice might help you understand. Or your son developing breasts. It does make me realise that the gatekeeping of puberty blockers and the huge waiting times for GIDS (Gender Identity Service) appointments for young trans people are literally harming and killing them.

For me though, the self-awareness or the courage to connect was just not there.

I have read on a forum that testosterone, while usually the enemy of the trans female body, is also able to mask and compensate for the dysphoria caused by not having oestrogen. Testosterone can give a single-mindedness and a determination. It provides energy to do, and get on, and it stops the tendency to sit and reflect. Whether this is scientifically true or not, I don't know. But it does fit my experience. At a point in my life where my male body began its slowdown hormonally, around 40, I was married with a family of three. It took three to four years of therapy and antidepressants before I could even attempt to deal with my darkest inner secret of crossdressing. I wanted to be able to own it, without shame. In the way Eddie Izzard or Grayson Perry seemed to be able to. So that's what I did. From being an 'occasional' and shameful 'cross dresser', I started to hold back the shame. The world was changing, and so could I. Except the more I explored with gender presentation and expression, the more my pain intensified. Then I read an online blog by Zinnia Jones, a trans woman who lists her own experience of 'gender dysphoria', and my world fell apart. It was number eight that I found most frightening.

Zinnia describes her eight points as:

1. Continual difficulty getting through the day.
2. A sense of misalignment, disconnect, or estrangement from your own emotions.
3. A feeling of just going through the motions in life, as if reading from a script.
4. A seeming pointlessness to your life, no sense of meaning or purpose.
5. Knowing you are somehow different but wishing you could be normal.
6. A notable escalation during puberty.
7. Attempting to fix things with coping mechanisms (alcohol/drugs).
8. Substantial resolution of symptoms through transitioning and particularly through HRT.[1]

The unravelling of gender dysphoria and my own eventual transition was not instantaneous by any stretch of the imagination. And it was not without professional guidance in therapy and, eventually, from a GIC (Gender Identity Clinic). It was something that was going to be, from the outset, the end of my marriage, so it wasn't something that I would choose to do without time, care, and consideration. My ex and I are not together now, although we were for longer than either of us expected. Sometimes sexuality can be fluid, but other times not. We remain close friends and, I think, fantastic co-parents to our children.

When I had, for the first time ever, spoken aloud my worries about gender dysphoria (to my own GP, who had previously been outstanding in every way), my gushed, 'I'm worried I might be a transsexual' was dismissed as, 'That would mean you actually want to *be* a woman, and you're definitely not in that category'. When I shared Zinnia's list, again, I was dismissed. 'These things are depression or anxiety'. The notion of dissociative personality disorder was also mentioned. The route prescribed to me was not a GIC, but a psychiatric appointment at the local hospital. After months of waiting I shared my fears with a psychiatrist who again dismissed me. I was (he said) a man. He asked me if I liked to watch lesbians in porn. I didn't ever watch porn, incidentally. He then told me that he 'knows men' and all men 'like watching lesbians'. I wanted, he explained, 'to imagine I was a lesbian to f**k with my wife'. Again, I tried to show him Zinnia's list. He didn't even glance at it. Much later, I learned that he was referencing 'autogynephilia'. A deeply problematic, discredited, and actually quite offensive label for trans women that shifts dysphoria into a sexual fetish about seeing themselves sexually as women. That intervention, and the opinion of a second psychiatrist who refused to refer me to a GIC until my depression was under control, added at least two years to my waiting time.

All of the factors mentioned by Zinnia were intensifying at this point. I felt like a kettle about to explode. It took a year of appointments with a specialist at the gender clinic to actually prescribe oestrogen. The effects were immediate.

Pre-oestrogen I had always been hot. Boiling hot. Angry hot. The kind of hot that stops you being able to think calmly or clearly. This ran through pretty much every aspect of my life. Truthfully, this is still a feature of my body I find difficult sometimes, but the shift was seismic nonetheless. My anger and temper had been almost unbearable. That doesn't help with being a partner, or a parent. Shifts in mood were quick and powerful. My existence was constantly wound up. Unless I drank alcohol. Which would lift the discomfort for an evening, ready for a return (with depression) the following day. As the initially low dose of oestrogen hit my body's receptors, there was an immediate change. Profound but also subtle. I started to feel like I was inhabiting my body and had connections to it. Previously I used to imagine and visualise I was made of metal, in some of my most stressed moments. I would imagine being magnetically slammed against walls and ceilings, and corners of walls in the house. I remember asking my partner if she ever imagined this, as though it were just part of being human. I don't know why I was surprised when she said she didn't. Her reaction and care about me because of these daydreams surprised me. But they are no longer part of my life.

I wasn't able to cry before. And not because I didn't believe men should. I felt detached from my own feelings and emotions, kept apart from them by invisible barriers that seemingly nobody could identify or pinpoint. Another memory that so clearly brings this home to me was a point when a very dear and close friend nervously told me, at the end of a night out, that they were terminally ill. It felt painful and shocking and sad, but I felt myself almost outside of my corporeal body – I felt like I was in a soap opera. I did cry for that friend, much later, and I cried for my dad when he died. But the tears, and the shuddering, and the gasps for breath felt artificial and false. I yearned to have the connection to those emotions and feelings, but only after taking oestrogen have I been able to do that.

I had a very close work friend around this time who had recently started HRT for her menopause. We both laughed a great deal as we discussed remarkably similar experiences pre-HRT. While her endocrine system stopped producing the oestrogen that allowed her to feel 'normal', mine had never produced the balance I needed. The fact that an identical medication could relieve symptoms so dramatically and clearly in two people with biologically different bodies seemed to warrant a far greater understanding in a societal and medical context.

Of course, oestrogen is not the only hormone that affects dysphoria in trans women. There is also testosterone. As my hormone therapy progressed, I added a trimonthly injection to completely block testosterone (which at that point, my body was still producing in the unwanted small round factories between my legs). This reduced my body's testosterone levels to virtually zero and again, led to a fairly seismic improvement in my sense of self. Because of having bottom surgery, I don't need to continue 'blocking' but I do clearly remember the feeling as those injections wore off. It was supposed to last for 12 weeks, but in actuality, lasted only for ten. I would feel anger and tension again, and my brain was misted and easily distracted. I lost clarity and calm. I would usually work this out from my feelings, then call the doctors to see when I needed to have the injection and it was nearly always in two weeks' time. It's interesting to note that my friend, a trans man, took a blocker to stop his oestrogen. He adds testosterone through a gel. His experience of the blocker running out early was almost identical to mine. But while I needed oestrogen and felt worse with testosterone, he was the polar opposite. Which again would seem to warrant more research and understanding about being an individual, and needing a holistic and unique approach to one's hormonal balance.

In Britain, just after the end of World War II, Alan Turing (and many other men) were given enforced conversion therapy to stop their homosexuality. Turing was 'chemically castrated' using oestrogen. He was incarcerated as well, but his eventual suicide could be seen as him escaping a chemically imposed gender dysphoria. Any attempt to find the evidence for 'male and female brains' has failed, and is always likely to because of the nuance around that question; the diversity of people's body chemistry, as well as their experience, is too vast. Being trans is not being 'a man trapped in a woman's body' or vice versa. But my own lived experience, and those of many friends, do lead me to think that the believed biological basis to being transgender is real. Until a point in time where healthcare providers and medical science are prepared to actually see female bodies, trans bodies, and Black bodies as being valid, to listen to the voices coming from those bodies, and to hear, act on, and validate those experiences, I worry that we are trapped in a cycle of gatekeeping, dismissal, misdiagnoses, inappropriate treatments, and loss of lives.

What next?

- **Mermaids UK** (*mermaidsuk.org.uk*) – Mermaids has been supporting trans and gender-diverse children, young people, and their families since 1995.

roaccutane tubes

on navigating puberty, hormones, and bodily changes in the wake of sexual abuse

by Madeleine Dunne

THE BATHROOM CABINET in my childhood home is a monument to my acne-stricken puberty. Rows of perfectly preserved lotions, wipes, and creams, littered with empty, cut-in-half Roaccutane tubes. I don't get nostalgic, not very often. Especially not for my awkward teenage years. But there's a prickle of fondness when I think about those angry, red spots.

Don't stop reading – I promise this isn't a lament about how acne isn't so bad, or some coming of age struggle to find my perfect £150 skincare routine. This is about puberty: that incessantly awkward rush of hormones that made us gross, angry, sad, horny, and hairy. It's about a body changing much faster than you'd like it to, and how childhood trauma resurfaces when we start to want the very things that hurt us. Sound good? Let's go.

It was the summer when all the boys traded in grass-stained knees for clumpy blue hair gel. It was the summer the girls embraced the style of *Hollyoaks* a bit too enthusiastically, weighing ourselves down with backcombed fringes gone hard with mum's hairspray, layers of Dream Matte Mousse foundation and those clunky bronze owl necklaces. It was the summer of drinking, where we'd slip crumpled tenners into the hands of older friends to grab us Blue WKD, Glen's, Lambrini, and no-brand cola. It was the summer we kicked off an intro into economics, saved up our pocket money for ten decks of Chesterfields, touted a single snout for £1 each to kids with stricter parents than us. It was the summer I kissed a girl and a boy, and decided I liked them just the same. It was the summer of drawing chodey cocks on people's Bebo wall and changing our MSN names to obscure MeWithoutYou lyrics. It was, most importantly, the summer puberty hit us all like a freight train.

Okay, not quite a freight train. More like a slow-burning match finally reaching the flint. At the edge of 15, most of us had already spent a few years in the throes of hormone-induced transfiguration. You've got Ashley, who had suddenly got tits and her period in second year, immediately warranting us to treat her with the utmost matriarchal respect and trust. But then again, you've got wee Ben, hardly reaching our shoulders and shouting at us in a voice that hadn't even started to do that baw-drop induced crackling.

My upbringing was an open and honest one. My sex education teachers were young, laughing with us as we awkwardly fit flavoured condoms onto wooden dildos and felt testicle-shaped bean bags for lumps. At lunch breaks down the lane where we smoked away from CCTV, we frankly discussed the average penis size, how Ben was absolutely, categorically lying about his, who still had virgin lips, and if we could borrow a tampon, please? There was an electrifying excitement around this puberty, palpable anticipation for the monumental change to our bodies this would bring.

Of course, this herd mentality wasn't how we all felt on the inside. For me, the tail end of puberty unlocked a Pandora's box of issues I'd never addressed.

I had been sexually abused by someone outside of my family. That's always the hardest bit to write – what happened. But it's a basic fact, one I accept has and will continue to shape me for most of my life. And that fact is all I'm going to write on this, because this isn't an essay about the act of sexual abuse. It's about the impact, and I won't give the act any more weight by offering further description. When survivors share their stories with us, we are quick to ask them for details: what happened, how old were you, where did it happen? Questions which make sense for curiosity's sake, sure, but when framing a discussion on how sexual abuse feeds into later life, there is a much more important question. When did you realise this happened to you?

Memory repression is a funny thing. It's our brain protecting us, a common reaction to trauma in early life. Unravelling that blocked out information can come slow or fast and can be triggered by the simplest things. Maybe it was viewing porn for the first time, or maybe accidently seeing your parents have sex. For me, it was watching my body pass through those very final stages of puberty.

I hated my body. I hated the tiny red pin pricks left behind when I shaved the prickly hair on my legs. I hated the debilitating growing pains in my limbs, when my frame suddenly lurched from chubby and short to tall and lanky. I hated having breasts, body parts that seemed obtusely sexual in their very nature. I hated my face; my angry, red, spot-ridden face and all the puss I could imagine congregating underneath the surface. Biologically, these rapid changes signalled the abrupt ending of my childhood. And as my hormones raced and I found myself getting the hots for people and horny little thoughts creeping in, it signalled the conflicting notion that soon, sex would likely be a regular part of my life.

Sexual abuse lingers. Even when the experience hasn't been fully processed, there is a desperate desire to cling onto some semblance of control. When it started to feel like my own body was betraying me, I stubbornly tried to reverse it. I tried every over-the-counter acne treatment I could find. I exercised excessively and starved myself. I bound my chest with tight sports bras or bandages. I took the long, curly hair that I'd spend years growing and cut it short and blunt. To me, these actions represented rejecting imposed femininity, a safeguard against being sexualised.

Even if my body hadn't changed, I think I would have had this weird period of mourning. After that summer when my puberty hit, I suddenly became unbearably sad. Not the kind of sad that comes about when your eyes prick at the end of *It's A Wonderful Life* or your cat has been missing for a week, but a heavy, lingering one. The kind of sadness that tightens in your chest and curls up around your lungs, sending you into blind panics when you think about it too much.

Years later I'd come to recognise that sadness as depression and anxiety. But back then, I wasn't equipped to understand why these hormonal changes triggered such distress. As an adult bolstered with the support of therapy, I can approach it with basic facts: I had been sexually abused as a child by someone outside of my family, and exposure to the stress of traumatic events at a young age increases the risk of developing mental health disorders. Those feelings and reactions might not have seemed rational at the time, but the clarity of a context I didn't fully comprehend yet made them totally understandable.

I wish more than anything that I could go back and explain all of this to myself, hold her and tell her that everything starts to hurt less. But I can't. No one can. Like many victims of abuse, I suffered alone. I learned how to bury things deep inside of me and carried the weight through to adulthood.

I hate being called brave, and I hate being called tough. I didn't ask for someone to do that to me when I was a kid; my resilience was always just survival instinct. But I won't do that teenage girl a disservice by ending this on a sympathetic note. She *was* tough; cantankerous as she asked for help for issues she didn't understand. That desperate desire to be in control manifested as a desperate desire to be alive, and I am eternally grateful that she had the sense and will to start unpacking these issues so early.

By the time the next summer came around, the boys still wore that same hair gel. The girls still made their hair hard with hairspray, but we'd found fake tan and started trying out too-orange foundation by then. We still drank in fields, and we still sold single cigarettes for extortionate prices. I lathered on Roaccutane and my cracked, dry skin made me mourn my angry spots. Our hormones were raging, and we became increasingly more awkward around the genders we found attractive. I kissed girls, and I kissed boys, and I felt confident that I was placing my lips on people I liked because I wanted to. When we all started having sex, I'd make the firm decision to do it while watching *The O.C.* because I liked the person, and because I wanted to. Awkward and clumsy, sure, but those are the sexual experiences I remember fondly as my firsts. Because I liked the person, and because I wanted to do them.

Of course, this account is just a tiny frame of the wider experience. There were still struggles – I was still sad, and I'd remain so for a long, long time. My adulthood would see my relationship with sex ebb and flow between emotionally exhaustive and fundamentally freeing, a weapon to punish myself or an unhealthy source of validation. My relationship with my body remained one of control and anger. But summers like those are the ones I can look back on and say weren't taken from me. They aren't repressed or confusing;

they are crystalline examples that childhood sexual abuse can shape a person without ruling every aspect of their life. They are non-ambiguous pieces of evidence that control can be taken back without the caveat of harming yourself. They are shards of light in the darkest place of your mind. They are a reason to shut the bathroom cabinet with a smile.

What next?

- **The National Association for People Abused in Childhood** (*napac.org.uk*) – NAPAC is the UK's leading national charity offering support to adult survivors of all types of childhood abuse.

withholding

by Clare Marie Edgeman

I'M NOT SURE which woke me up first, the pressure in my bladder or the slight wetness in between my thighs, but it only took a moment for the horror to wash through me. I was about to wet my friend's bed. I scooched to the edge of Lisa's bed, quickly and quietly stepping over her as she slept on a mattress taking up the entirety of the floor space in her small room, and ran for the bathroom.

I sat down on the intimidating, automated toilet and tried to relax. I'd last peed only two hours before, around midnight; was it really this bad? Was I down to only two hours of possible sleep? Tears leaked from my eyes and I cried as I peed for the second time that night. I would be up three more times before Lisa and her family woke to start the day. The dry, cotton tackiness of my mouth wasn't abated by the glasses of water I kept quietly pouring myself in the kitchen after each bathroom visit.

'Are you okay?'

The day before, I'd had one of the happiest moments of my entire life as I'd pulled on Gap jeans in a tiny Tokyo dressing room. They were a size I hadn't been since I was 13 years old. They looked amazing. I felt amazing. Except I didn't. I felt like I was dying. Walking more than a mile at a time was becoming difficult. I was desperately thirsty all the time.

But I was skinny. Finally.

I'd tried to be skinny before, but never succeeded. In my earlier teens I'd been a failure at both anorexia and bulimia. I just liked food too much and I was absolute shit at making myself throw up. But then I was diagnosed with Type 1 diabetes. And after that diagnosis, I discovered what I would call the 'High Diet'.

The 'High Diet' was simple: withhold insulin, lose weight.

I found out about the possibility of withholding insulin to lose weight when my paediatric endocrinologist gave me a book that warned teenage girls about the dangers of skipping doses to lose weight. I'd not previously realised it was a possibility. I read between the lines of the warning and decided that I could do this safely. I wouldn't withhold *all* my insulin. I didn't want to end up in a coma. But if I withheld *some* of my insulin, my body would be unable to process carbohydrates. I could eat all the junk food I wanted and my body just wouldn't process the carbohydrates. Instead, I would pee them out. The best part about the 'High Diet' was that it appeared that I was eating like any normal teenager. It took a high-level understanding of the nuances of insulin and Type 1 diabetes to see that I was killing myself to be thin.

Type 1 diabetes is an autoimmune disorder where a diabetic's body stops producing insulin. This differs greatly from Type 2 diabetes. A Type 2 diabetic's body stops being able to use their own insulin. That is called insulin resistance. It is scary and dangerous and can lead to all kinds of complications, but it is nothing like Type 1. I never really know what to say when someone asks me if I have the 'bad' kind of diabetes, but considering that mismanagement of Type 1 diabetes can have imminent, life-threatening consequences, I'm comfortable assuming they mean Type 1, and yes, I do have the 'bad' kind of diabetes.

If a Type 1 diabetic doesn't inject insulin into their body, they will die in a matter of days. Without insulin, a human body is unable to process carbohydrates, and no matter what the latest diet trends tell you, we need carbs to live.

Prior to my diagnosis I'd failed at withholding food, but I was a champion at withholding insulin. So for several months over the course of my final year of high school, I took some, but not too much. I let my blood sugars run dangerously high, but not high enough to cause any terrible complications, at least not in the short term.

However, as I sat on my friend's bed in Tokyo early on a cold January morning in 2005, I knew I couldn't do this much longer. As I climbed back into bed and heard Lisa whisper,

'Are you okay?', I mumbled something about being fine, made an excuse about drinking lots of water before bed, and then softly started to cry into her pillow.

No, I finally started to admit to myself, I was not okay, but I couldn't say it out loud. Not yet.

Those tears were the start of an unravelling of sorts. I recognised that I couldn't go on this way indefinitely. With each tear cried into my friend's pillow, half a world away from my home in the mountains of Montana, I started to recognise that I didn't want to live this way anymore. It was such freedom to finally be thin, but it was coming at too high a cost.

In the months that followed, I slowly started taking my insulin in full doses again. It wasn't a complete and perfect recovery. That night in Tokyo wasn't a perfect 'aha' moment, but it was the first domino, cascading into others, and by the time I graduated high school in June 2005, I was taking my insulin in regular doses and had gained back a healthy amount of weight.

I was constantly tempted to return to the 'High Diet' over the course of my first year at New York University's prestigious Tisch School of the Arts. I was studying drama, had been accepted into the most exclusive program in the country, and diabulimia (as I'd recently learned my insulin-withholding 'diet' was officially named) was a nagging temptation in the back of my mind. I was out of my depth, thousands of miles from home, and desperate to belong, be seen, and be understood. I was told continuously how much my body didn't conform to 'leading lady' standards, and so I dieted, determined not to return to withholding insulin. However, the stress and the dieting, and the yo-yoing of my weight, took their toll. Before my first semester at NYU was finished, my stress and my determination *not* to withhold insulin had manifested as a binge eating disorder that would stay with me for nearly a decade.

I left NYU and found a smaller, cosier university where I could continue my education in Washington State. I went to therapy with an eating disorder specialist. She was kind, thoughtful, and well-intentioned. But therapy for eating disorders hinges on not counting and obsessing about food. This is an absolute impossibility for a Type 1 diabetic. How much insulin we dose is dependent on how many carbohydrates we eat. Ideally, everything is counted and measured, and appropriate doses are given. This obsessive attention to detail of what is in every bit of food we eat is what keeps diabetics alive.

I turned to 'holistic' answers. I turned to veganism and raw foods for a few months and truly felt amazing. I fasted and pretended that it was about feeling good as I got on the scale every morning to track my weight. And I binged health food and junk food and truly any kind of food in an attempt to numb out the 'shoulds' and ringing truths that my body just wasn't small enough for my dreams. Even in the smaller theatre department of my new, much less prestigious acting school, I was cast as the old women and the aunties. I was costumed in caftans and robes.

Eventually, in my mid-twenties, I replaced binge eating with binge fucking – turning to promiscuity to fill a void. And strangely, and almost magically, it was a much healthier option for me and taught me a hell of a lot about myself and other people. Promiscuity introduced me to my body in a whole new way. I discovered what my body could feel, and how it could make others feel, and it began to feel more and more like a site of experience rather than something to be tolerated or managed. Slowly but surely, I found myself recovering from binge eating, and eventually falling in love and settling into a much steadier life than I'd ever imagined.

Recovery is a strange thing when binging is your self-destructive indulgence of choice. Food is everywhere, and over-indulging is a totally normal, even celebrated, behaviour. I still occasionally binge, but I tap into how my body and spirit feels when I do so and find that I don't need it in the same way I used to. I've banished words like 'cheat' from my vocabulary with regards to food. I've embraced the power of words to frame my experience of this life and so I 'indulge' rather than 'cheat'.

Yes, I still over-indulge, but I no longer feel the need to punish myself for it. I stand up to my doctors when they use words like 'obese' and then confirm that my bloodwork is good. I follow inspiring, beautiful fat women on social media to train my brain to see bodies like mine as beautiful.

I am healing, but I don't consider myself 'recovered'. Sixteen years after I stopped withholding insulin, I still struggle with disordered eating and the complex web of shame and self-worth. I've published a book where I go into vulnerable detail about body-image, sex, diabetes, and diabulimia, and yet I still had to unfollow almost every diabetic influencer on my Instagram feed when COVID-19 took over all of our lives.

Isolation became time for optimisation, and diabetics with big followings showed their followers how we can use this time to not only survive, but optimise. How perfect can your blood sugars be? How many squats can you do to balance your hormones? What does your quarantine workout look like and what are your blood sugars before and after? I have no interest in optimisation. Optimisation is too close to obsessive control, and obsessive control is what leads me down the rabbit hole into the worst versions of myself.

And here I am, 50 days into our COVID quarantine, and I almost couldn't write this essay. My biggest fear in sharing my story of diabulimia is that a young diabetic will read it not as a cautionary tale, but as inspiration. I remember 'pro-ana' corners of the internet and how much they stick in the recesses of my psyche to this day. However, I know stories of survival, of slow and quiet evolution, are important.

The patience and compassion I've learned to show myself about my chronic illness I now must extend to my ability to create and share in a world being shaped by a deadly virus. The isolation and restriction I've felt so acutely at various stages of my life is now being mirrored back to me on a cultural scale. My partner and I eat pasta at least three times a week, we indulge in chocolate and have a freezer full of ice cream. And for the first time in my life, I'm taking things one day at a time.

It now feels as though the world is withholding from us all, and I'm grateful for my precious supply of insulin and I'm not, for one moment, tempted to skip a dose.

What next?

- **Beyond Type 1** (*beyondtype1.org*) – Beyond Type 1 is a nonprofit organisation changing what it means to live with diabetes. Through platforms, programmes, resources, and grants, Beyond Type 1 is uniting the global diabetes community and providing solutions to improve lives today.

don't tell me to calm down

the politics of stress, rest, and lion taming

by L C Elliott

I NEVER WANTED to be the madwoman in the attic. That's why I work downstairs.

I don't remember writing those words, but I found them in my notes folder recently, dated about two years ago. At the time, I was ending my second year mostly housebound, after a whiplash injury and a series of infections left me with a bizarre array of symptoms that kept me firmly tethered to my sofa. I was in pain, permanently dizzy, exhausted, and scared. I was also grappling with the idea that I might be losing my mind.

It was a reasonable enough fear at the time, given that it was what most of my doctors had implied over the years. There was Dr W—, the kindly GP, who looked at my normal blood test results and gently suggested that my recent graduation might have stressed me out; there was Dr R—, the not-so-kindly ENT, who thought my persistent vertigo was because 'there were a lot of hills in Sheffield'; and there was Dr B—, the infuriating GP, who took one look at my left-sided tremor and asked if I thought I might have 'partial anxiety'.

I don't know about you, but I'd never heard of a graduation causing anyone to become housebound within a year. I barely restrained myself from asking Dr R— whether he realised we were in Yorkshire, not Nepal, and I've spent many a night wondering if Dr B— was seriously suggesting that my left side might be more anxious about the world than my right. But whether kindly or ridiculous, each doctor shared the same opinion: there was nothing physically wrong with me. My real problem was that I was stressed.

The issue for me wasn't whether or not I was stressed, or even whether or not I had anxiety. After all, after having to give up work, and becoming a reluctant prisoner in my own home, wasn't I entitled to a little bit of anxiousness about my life? My problem was that I couldn't convince my doctors that my anxiety had a physical, not a mental cause.

But was I right, or were they?

If they were right, then my pain, my intermittent paralysis, my slurred speech, headaches, vertigo, adrenaline rushes, fainting, and persistent tremor were all caused by stress. If I was right, then something physical was going very wrong inside my body, and no one was trying to help me. I couldn't help but think that if a man had presented with my symptoms, he would at least have been offered a brain scan. Instead, I was offered meditation and antidepressants, and ushered out of the door.

No wonder I became fixated on the madwoman in the attic.

Hysteria (n.), from the Greek '*hystera*' for 'womb'

The idea that 'nervous stress' was the cause of mental illness, and that women were more susceptible to psychosomatic symptoms than men, didn't originate with the Victorians, but it was popularised by them. For that, we have Charles Darwin to thank. In *The Descent of Man*[1] in 1871, he argued that man, through natural selection, had become superior to woman in courage, energy, intellect, and inventive genius.

It wasn't long before the sociologist Herbert Spencer[2] took his ideas further, claiming that human development depended upon the expenditure of a 'fixed fund of energy', which was fed through the nervous system like a battery. Since women depleted their energy in the reproductive process, he argued, they were developmentally arrested in intellectual competition with men.

For Darwinian psychiatrists, like the influential Henry Maudsley, there was 'sex in mind as distinctly as there is sex in the body', and it clearly, physiology marked women 'for very different offices in life to those of men'.[3] So, if a woman rejected domestic life and concentrated her efforts on work and politics, then was it any wonder that she became insane? Simply put, the stress of learning and work would deplete her fixed fund of energy, causing mental disturbance and preventing her from bearing children.

And so, while the spectre of the madwoman haunted the pages of Victorian novels, her real-life counterparts were admitted to asylums at ever increasing rates. The hysteric of the time, with her sexual forwardness and irritability, was the most troublesome. Meanwhile, the often-bedbound neurasthene, with her blushing, vertigo, headaches, neuralgia, and depression, charmed the doctors of the day. Of the many treatments offered to each woman, most had their roots in stress management.

In her book, *The Female Malady*, Elaine Showalter writes that for the hysterics in the asylums, 'the women's work most highly touted for its therapeutic efforts was laundry. Presumably, the aggressive activity of pounding the wet clothes, wringing them out, hanging them, and ironing, was thought to be a useful and effective outlet for [their] superfluous nervous energy'.[4] And, of course, it served the added bonus of reinforcing 'proper' social norms for troublesome women who resented their lot.

But while the hysteric was made to endure domestic drudgery, the female neurasthene, who was thought to suffer from a deficiency in nervous energy, was more frequently prescribed the rest cure. This meant force-feeding, strict bed rest, no study of any kind, and a total reliance on other people for their basic needs. It's little wonder that for many, the enforced isolation and boredom exacerbated their symptoms, and in probably the most famous story about the cure, the protagonist of *The Yellow Wallpaper*[5] hallucinates a woman trapped in the walls of her 'atrocious nursery', fighting bitterly to get out.

Trapped between the four walls of my own home, and suffering through my very own sickness-enforced rest cure, I grappled with the ghost of my former life taunting me from outside. In the twenty-first century, it's easy to feel as though we've come a long way from gendered ideas of mental illness, but what I was hearing from my doctors was that, at heart, I was a modern day neurasthene. This was all the more frustrating, because I'd been exquisitely, deliriously happy when I got sick, and I was as certain as anyone could be that my problem was a physical one. But if it wasn't nervous stress that was making me sick, then why did I feel as though my body was bubbling over with adrenaline?

The invention of stress

The very word 'stress' is ubiquitous nowadays, and being stressed has become something of a badge of honour. After all, if you're stressed out, you must be working hard, right? But stress, as we understand it, didn't exist until the 1930s, when it was discovered by a Hungarian physician called Hans Seyle.

As a student at the German Medical School in Prague, Hans made a very simple observation: that no matter what a patient was sick with, whether it was heart disease, tonsillitis, or the flu, they all simply 'looked sick'. This led him to theorise that there was a 'general syndrome of sickness', which wasn't unique to a single disease, but instead was a marker of most, and perhaps even of all, diseases.

Years later, during a serendipitous laboratory accident, he discovered that the single unifier was stress. But this wasn't stress in the Victorian sense of fragile nerves and limited energy. It wasn't even stress in my doctor's sense of mental strain. It was, instead, something that Hans called *biologic stress*, and the General Adaptation Syndrome.

In his seminal book, *The Stress of Life*,[6] Hans describes stress as 'the nonspecific response of the body to any demand', and says he first recognised it 'by evidence of adrenal stimulation, shrinkage of lymphatic organs, and sudden loss of body weight'. But more than this, the stress reaction, he discovered, wasn't necessarily a bad thing unless it was prolonged. Instead, it was the body's defence system which occurred in three well-defined stages.

The first stage was the alarm reaction, or fight-or-flight. In this stage, your heart rate increases, your adrenal glands release cortisol, and you receive a boost of adrenaline. Crucially, this happens in the same way whether a person is under mental stress, or if their body comes under attack by a disease, or experiences an injury.

But, as Hans discovered, 'no living organism can be maintained continuously in a state of alarm', and if the body survives the initial alarm reaction, it enters the second stage: the stage of resistance. In this stage, the body adapts and attempts to maintain a new normal by reversing the effects of the alarm reaction. Instead of releasing stress hormones into the blood, it keeps an excess locked in reserve, and rather than increasing metabolism, it slows it down until the body steadily accumulates weight. Finally, if the stress continues, it enters the third and final stage: the stage of exhaustion.

Of this stage, Hans writes that it is 'strikingly similar to the initial alarm reaction. At the end of a life under stress, [there was] a kind of premature aging due to wear and tear'. Eventually, at the end of this stage, the body simply gives up and dies.

But even though Hans had identified the stress reaction as a protective, not a destructive response, the concept of stress, he found, was inextricably linked with sickness – and it was far from a new discovery at all. Twenty-five centuries ago, Hippocrates, the Father of Medicine, told his disciples in Greece that disease is not only suffering (*pathos*), but also toil (*pónos*); it is the fight of the body to restore itself towards normal. Disease is not mere surrender to an attack, but also a fight for health, because unless there's a fight, there's no disease.

Hans identified that this fight is at the heart of the stress reaction, writing that 'disease is not just suffering, but a fight to maintain the homeostatic balance of our tissues, despite damage. There must be stress here, at least [as] the engineer speaks of stress and strain in the interaction of force and resistance'.

Biologic stress, then, is an inevitable part of all sickness, without which we would all simply die. So, the Victorians were at least partially right. Nervous stress can cause biologic stress, and while locking women away in asylums and forcing them to do laundry – or nothing at all – probably did more to increase their stress than to diminish it, they had identified the culprit, if not the cure. In fact, recent studies show that when activated, one key stress receptor can send signals to certain immune cells and change how they defend the body; leading to a number of allergic and inflammatory diseases.[7]

But if nervous stress can cause biologic stress, then the same can happen in reverse. The problem between me and my doctors, then, was one of language, as much as it was one of medicine.

The lion and the lion tamer

Biologic stress and nervous stress. Two different causes, the same singular stress reaction. But aside from being a necessity of life, stress – what kind, who has it, and why – has always been political. As late as the mid-twentieth century, while the female neurasthenes were confined, the male neurasthenes were celebrated. In America, the idea that neurasthenia was triggered by a limited fund of energy being depleted by stress proved that the male sufferer had a healthy work ethic.

If men spent too much time indoors and couldn't keep pace with their work, they were then susceptible to the effects of nervous stress. Women, however, were thought to be susceptible only when they became too socially active, and spent too much time outside the home taxing their thoughts with politics and work. Consequently, the treatment for men was to get outside and exercise in the fresh air, while for women, it was the rest cure.

If a man suffered from a stress-induced illness, it was proof of his masculine hard work and drive. If a woman suffered from the same, it was proof that she was constitutionally incapable of working at the same level as men. Women were beset by lions, and men were simply better at lion taming.

I said before that it's easy to think that we don't gender illness the same way. But less than a hundred years since Hans Seyle identified the stress reaction, gendered ideas of sickness, and in particular of nervous vs. biologic stress, still play a large role in our healthcare. Today, women have a 50% higher chance of receiving a false diagnosis following a heart attack[8] because they're more likely to be told they're having a panic attack.

Numerous studies have found that doctors are more likely to assume chronic pain in women is caused by emotional distress, *even when clinical tests prove otherwise*.[9] And even though around 75% of people affected by autoimmune illnesses are women, it takes an average of five different specialists and 4.6 years[10] for us to receive a correct diagnosis, with many receiving false mental health labels along the way.

The limits of our language compound the issue further, because stress is both lion and lion tamer. Both cause and effect. It is the marker of sickness, and at the same time, the evidence of health. The distinction between 'stress' the causative event and 'stress' the reaction is so loose that Hans Seyle had to coin the word 'stressor' to distinguish the trigger of stress from the biologic reaction to it. But at a certain point, the stress reaction feeds itself; it is a circular problem.

And so, we circle back to the problem with my doctors. They were arguing that stress was the egg and I was arguing it was the chicken. Meanwhile, the reality was that a great cosmic rooster was flapping around the room knocking everything off-balance and making one hell of a racket, and only I could see its effects.* But whether mental or physical, my stress had become political, and I was fighting not only the reaction, but a battle with the medical profession to be taken seriously.

Three years on from the onset of my symptoms, I received the first of many diagnoses from a private neurologist: hypermobile Ehlers-Danlos Syndrome, a connective tissue disorder. Almost a year to the day, a vestibular doctor – a balance specialist – finally identified the source of my 'anxiety'. Complications from my weak connective tissue, combined with a whiplash injury and a raft of infections, had damaged my balance system. Consequently, my body was being sent signals that it was falling, triggering a near-constant release of adrenaline. I was living inside a perpetual alarm reaction.

Practically, if not biologically, this makes a difference. I could have taken anti-anxiety medication until the cows came home – or the cosmic rooster dropped to the ground, exhausted – and I would never have seen any improvement. Now, I complete vestibular exercises every day, in the hope that my balance nerves will learn to compensate, and put an end to the chronic stress syndrome.

No organism can live in a constant state of alarm, Hans Seyle said, and so far, I'm proving him right. Despite the

---

* *Note to my doctors: this is a metaphor. I am not and have never hallucinated cosmic roosters.*

frequent adrenaline rushes, I spend most of my time in the stage of resistance, conserving energy, trying not to exceed the reduced capacity of my body, and, between you and me, steadily gaining weight.

Like the Victorian neurasthene, I am still confined to my home most of the time, but since my diagnosis, I feel less like the madwoman in the attic. What I've discovered in the interim is that stress is a part of all of our lives, and it has been since life formed a second cell. But exactly who's allowed to be stressed, by what, and to what degree, is still more often a question of politics than it is one of medicine.

What next?

- **Society for Women's Health Research** (*swhr.org*) – The Society for Women's Health Research (SWHR) is a national nonprofit dedicated to improving women's health through science, policy, and education; raising awareness of gender bias in medical trials and campaigning to have women included at every stage of research and testing.

telling hormonal stories

by Sonja Erikainen, Andrea Ford,
Roslyn Malcolm, and Lisa Raeder

HORMONES ARE THE subject of many different kinds of stories. In popular culture, they play roles in many social activities and identities – for example, oxytocin is thought to be the substance of love, and cortisol the manifestation of stress, while testosterone seems like the essence of masculinity, and oestrogen carries the spirit of femininity. Hormones are characters in stories that can be both empowering and oppressive, plural and diverse, sometimes inconsistent with each other, and often vague and fragmented. We tell them to and about ourselves and each other in ways that affect our daily lives.

These stories are pieced together from multiple sources – from what we are told by other people in our lives, from the popular media, from our own experiences. It might be tempting to look towards biology and medicine to find clarity and discover the 'true story' about the nature of hormones, as a way to resolve the conflicting stories we hear and tell ourselves. Yet, in medicine just as in popular culture, what hormones are, what they can do, and to whom are stories that are continually re-interpreted. Scientists observe new things about hormones and write their observations down as scientific stories that other people can read.

While hormones were once understood to be 'internal secretions' of the body that naturally set various physical processes 'in motion' on their own, today the hormones our bodies produce are influenced and controlled medically, including via hormone-based medical treatments and therapies. For example, administering extra hormones like oestrogen and progesterone into our bodies is often seen as a desirable and 'normal' part of everyday life for women and people who menstruate: hormonal contraceptives are seen to enable us to gain control over our sexual and reproductive bodies, while (especially women's) bodies that are not controlled in this way are often seen to be 'unruly', hormonally out of 'balance'. Likewise, suppressing the production of cortisol, or adding more oxytocin, is seen to enable us to take control over our 'imbalanced' (stressed out, anxious, autistic) brains. It is hard to distinguish between what's 'biological' and what's 'social' in the way these stories play out.

As anthropologists and sociologists, we research how different kinds of stories about hormones fit together and influence each other. Our job is not to determine which stories are 'true' and which are not. They are all true insofar as they have real effects in the world. Our task is to highlight how these stories fit into broader cultural trends and are produced within the values and beliefs of a specific time and place. We have compiled some of the stories that are familiar to us and may be familiar to you. Which stories do you recognise? What stories do you tell, and about whom?

Oxytocin

'It's a male brain thing. Too much testosterone in the womb. Don't you know the ratio?'[1]

It's seven to one…no, five to one…maybe three to one male to female, depending on who you ask. The rates are in fact uncertain. But the takeaway? 'Yes, more boys than girls'.

Why is autism gendered in this way? Why is it still seen as a male condition, leaving many autistic women to keep advocating for their very existence? Are we just expected to get on with things more than men? To mask our problems? To socialise in 'nice', 'normal' ways, even when it goes against our wishes, or ways we would choose to engage?

Autism is kaleidoscopic, a diverse collection of ways of being in the world. It is gendered as predominantly male and framed as a condition of social issues, which might be the only aspects holding it together. There's no consensus over cause or best care, and hormones leak in to fill that gap.

Engaging in environments that do not understand what it is like being autistic is stressful, exhausting; sensorially, emotionally. 'It's too much cortisol flow, autism', they now say.

This explanation articulates the chronic stress experienced by some autistic people. Yet it silences the context, putting responsibility on the self rather than the situation.

The therapist tells me: 'There is luckily a hormone which has been found to counteract the corrosive effect of cortisol in the brain, and that is a hormone called oxytocin. Oxytocin is a hormone that goes by many names; the 'feel good hormone', the 'love hormone', the 'trust hormone'. It's a really nice hormone…'

Oxytocin nose spray is now offered as a treatment, she says. 'The natural kind is best though. It's really easy to produce. Rock your hips, hug, squeeze'.

'Oxytocin is…actually what kick-starts labour. It's released when a mother holds their child, rocks their child. It's released when you breastfeed, so it's really important for bonding'.

Some goddess of feminine connection, like Hera, oxytocin is seen to hold the power and promise of feminised love. She bonds people, opens them, makes them feel safe, cared for. Proximity and bodily pressure release her flows. She makes you want more. Feedback loops of love. Oxytocin exists in all human bodies, yet rarely do we hear of male oxytocin flows, father–child bonding.

Framing autism as some kind of hormonal 'imbalance', a lack of oxytocin and excess of testosterone, folds in older ideas around cold 'career women' with masculine, testosterone-filled wombs producing 'hyper-male brains' and social 'deficits'. It's your fault, they say. Not a lack of being understood or accepted as different. This difference from the 'normal' is something that we could all do better to understand.

Testosterone

'Testosterone is the big daddy of male sex hormones. It drives aggression and sexual violence, lust and machismo. It makes you a better athlete. It makes a man out of you'.

Testosterone regulates the development of physical characteristics like the growth of facial and body hair, deepening the voice, increasing muscle mass. Because testosterone is a male sex hormone, these characteristics, people say, are 'male sex characteristics'. They also say, though, that because these are male sex characteristics, testosterone is a male sex hormone. A vicious circle.

When I hear these things, I think of my own body, which was assigned 'female' at birth. I think of the testosterone that flows within it, shaping how it feels, looks, and works, and I think of the relationship between the testosterone flows and my non-binary gender identity. Nearly all human bodies, whether male, female, or otherwise, secrete testosterone from their testicles or ovaries and adrenal glands. Some bodies produce more than others – indeed, men generally produce more than women – but everyone needs testosterone to be healthy, irrespective of gender. Why, then, is testosterone male?

In international sport competitions, athletes who want to compete in women's sports need to be able to prove that they have only small amounts of testosterone in their bodies.[2] This is because testosterone is not only male but also a performance enhancing hormone, people say. It makes you stronger and faster. The reason why sports competitions are divided into separate women's and men's categories is that women, they say, are not strong or fast enough to compete against men, so separate women's sports are needed to provide women a fair chance to win. Testosterone is the 'essence' of sex difference in sports. It is the reason why women are weaker and slower than men. But what about non-binary bodies like mine? What about those of us whose sex and gender have no 'essence' to hang onto?

'Women' are not weaker and slower than 'men', *categorically*. Some women are bigger and stronger than some men, and women athletes competing in international sports can be bigger and stronger than most men. Men also don't have more testosterone than women *categorically*. Some men have the same amount as most women, and some women have as much as most men. When women have as much testosterone as men generally do, though, people say that the testosterone makes them too strong and too fast, 'for a woman'.

People say that if athletes try to enhance their performance by adding extra testosterone into their bodies, then they are doping, and doping is unfair. Not for everyone though. There's an exception, reserved for men who have less testosterone than men generally do.[3] These men are allowed to add extra testosterone into their bodies, because if they don't, then they are too weak and too slow, 'for a man', people say. I wonder how they would categorise me if I took extra testosterone, not enough 'for a man', yet too much 'for a woman'. Too weak and slow 'for a man', too strong and fast 'for a woman'. Too much and too little, at the same time.

People say these things. But who are they, the people who say? Scientists, sport regulators, your uncle, people down the pub. Did they know that human bodies regularly convert testosterone into oestrogen, 'the mother' of 'female' sex hormones? Do molecules have gender, and why would people say that they do? Did anyone ever ask testosterone what its gender identity is?

Oestrogen

'It's like we're going to be the hormone generation', said Linnea. The girls laughed in agreement. Linnea had just told the group how she, despite clearly stating that she preferred using condoms, had been prescribed the Pill by the midwife she had encountered at the youth clinic. The midwife had informed Linnea that 'it's for the best, you never know', which Linnea perceived as an expectation for her to reconsider her choice of contraception.

Klara continued: 'I remember I was talking to a midwife one time and he was like, 'You're in the risk zone!' It was insane and I was like, 'But why am I in the risk zone? What do you mean?' but he just kept going, 'You're in the risk zone!' while kind of standing there waving his fist at me. So, I said, 'But is it your body we're talking about?' He said no, so I said, 'Well then, if I want to be in the risk zone with my own body then isn't it my choice?''

'I don't understand – what risk zone?' Ellen asked.

'Me getting pregnant. But I didn't buy it, I've never been pregnant, I've never even had to have an abortion', Klara responded.

Hormonal contraceptives are usually understood to provide women with security, freedom of choice, and health.[4] Linnea and Klara, however, both explained to me how they feel reluctant to comply with the recommendations they receive. Instead, they expressed discomfort at the idea of manipulating the hormonal balances of their own bodies, and frustration that they're expected to 'do something' with their bodies when their (male) partners are not expected to do the same. Oestrogen and progesterone in the form of hormonal contraceptives are distributed on a global level and marketed as a biomedical technology *for* women.[5] Why, then, in this scenario, isn't the story of hormonal contraceptives as the tool for 'women's emancipation' the one that shapes Klara's and Linnea's experiences?

Instead, they rejected the narrative that self-administering oestrogen and progesterone induces feelings of security and control of the self, as well as the idea that their bodies are abject or 'risky' when not hormonally regulated.[6] Saga says that it is not her body, but the hormones she feels expected to take that pose a risk to her health. Frustrated, she explains how the midwife she met didn't take her concern seriously. 'And then I got angry because she basically said that there are no problems with the Pill, so I got quite annoyed and said that I don't know anyone – I know quite a few who [are] on the

Pill – but I don't know anyone who hasn't had problems with side effects. And she was like, 'Yes, but that's very uncommon', and I said, 'But I don't think it's *that* uncommon'. So, I got a bit angry because she was pretty much saying that the things I've experienced haven't happened, that it's not real. Stories about what is real or not shape how hormones mediate our lives.

Sofia called out the double standard in stories about contraceptive hormones. 'We're treated as if other people are supposed to tell us what to do, and then it's like, "Don't have unprotected sex, you can get pregnant!"' The girls nodded and recounted stories of feeling pressured by expectations that portray them as in need of hormonal contraceptives even when they themselves haven't expressed interest in using them. 'I've just felt more and more that I have no urge to stuff myself with things that I don't know what they are. I'm kind of scared of the whole thing', Klara sighed. 'I've never wanted it myself. It's just been something that I'm supposed to want to take'.

Cortisol

'The stress level of the mom determines what kind of egg she releases. If the mom is stressed, she produces a being with more emphasis on the midbrain, where the fight or flight instinct comes from, instead of the front brain, where thought and empathy happen'. Harmony explained this to me on a cool summer morning in Santa Cruz, California, where we had met to discuss mindfulness and childbirth education. 'It makes sense that a lot of cortisol production during [pregnancy] would make for a highly tuned nervous system in the baby. Cortisol, you know, the stress hormone'.

As I learned more about the stories surrounding cortisol, which has been called 'public enemy number one', I thought about how much this ties into our high-stress culture generally.[7] What if we could just blame it all on a hormone? Would that be easier than changing our way of life?

'It can start in the mom's health even before conception', Harmony said. No pressure. But really, could anything make a newly pregnant person more anxious than thinking that their anxiety had damaged their baby even before their baby existed? Well, a war zone maybe. Harmony noted this, self-deprecatingly.

Sure, cortisol turns food into energy, and manages blood pressure, and fights the good fight against inflammation. It dives into the bloodstream from those little adrenal glands, which are way down by the kidneys. So maybe we should blame the brain. The pituitary gland, the hypothalamus. They're the ones dishing out the instructions.

It's too much! Literally, there's just too much cortisol! Hanging around, causing obesity, causing diabetes, causing heart attacks. Causing depression. Need I go on? But I could go on. Bone density. Learning disorders. Inflammation. Weak immunity. Memory loss.

Couldn't cortisol just back off? Please?

All right, all right, I imagine our culture saying in response to medical stories about cortisol's damaging effects. Fine, we'll do some more meditation. Maybe take on a lighter load at work. Go to kickboxing class, or, obviously, yoga. Tell the kids their bad behaviour is making us sick, keep the guilt rolling.

They say 'feeling socially connected, safe, and self-reliant' reduces cortisol. They've got a lot of great ideas, don't they? They say 'tend and befriend' will counteract your 'fight and flight' program.[8] Recruit some oxytocin and dopamine to the party. But it's not like we can just opt out of society. A fearful, isolated, stressed-out society where we connect by browsing through alarmist news silos and curated food pics on social media, and brag about our overwork.

'Eustress' is like euphoria; that's cortisol at the top of its game, the can-do attitude, Flow State. Why doesn't it just re-engineer itself to only produce that? Enough with this 'distress', making us run in circles with nowhere to go.[9] Why won't *it* evolve, instead of us having to change? Because this is a pandemic! We're spreading cortisol around, even to those who aren't born yet! If we're going to keep seeing so much of it, if there's no exit to this high-cortisol way of life, it's high time it got its own act together.

Hormonal stories

Stories help us make sense of what hormonal problems count, who is responsible, and what is 'us' or 'not us', 'self' or 'other'. Hormones are 'made' and 're-made' in both scientific and cultural stories. Indeed, scientific and cultural stories are constantly in conversation with each other. Ways of understanding what hormones do, and to whom, change in the course of both scientific and social developments.

Hormones take on many biological, physical, social and cultural guises. Which hormones are good, and which are bad, to and for whom? What does it mean, both medically and socially, to lead a hormonally 'normal' or 'balanced' life? When is a body hormonally 'balanced', and when does an 'imbalance' become a problem that requires 'rebalancing' via medical means? What *are* hormones, in the end?

Hormones exist in the material world, in our bodies – but their identities and the roles that they play in our lives are as much about stories or narratives as they are about facts. We shape and make hormones' identities through the stories that we tell, as much as they shape and make us.

What next?

- **Black Women Birthing Justice**
  (*blackwomenbirthingjustice.org*) – Black Women Birthing Justice is a collective of Black, African American, African, Caribbean, and multiracial women who are committed to transforming birthing experiences for Black women and transfolks. Our vision is that that every pregnant person should have an empowering birthing experience, free of unnecessary medical interventions.
- ***Messengers of Sex*** by Celia Roberts

meron

by Rita Faire

Panimulang Bahagi

THEY SAID SHE was the spectre on the roof. A white figure stark against the night sky like the flashes of lightning around her. Her hands clasped at her chest, she defiantly raised her gaze to Heaven. For she was praying, you see — not casting spells like wagging tongues spread. No one below could hear the prayer. All they could hear was thunder.

'María Clara is dead!'

She died thirteen years later. Thirteen years after they locked her there. Thirteen years living a fate that she chose when there were no other choices left to her.

'The convent for me or the grave!' she'd once cried. So the convent it was. The convent it was for thirteen long years, atoning for sins that weren't her own.

The night on the roof, she prayed for salvation, freedom from men's hypocrisy. Freedom that came too late.

(Freedom that never came at all.)

María Clara is dead.

She died after suddenly taking ill. She died in her sleep, or so I like to think.

She died so that we could live.

But hundreds of years later, she's still not at rest and we're still trying to kill her.

i.

My period has always been painful.

Pale. Frail. Barely any energy to spare. Only enough for the essentials. Eat something (even if it was just a little). Go to the bathroom. Change my pad. Crying some days, just gritting my teeth and hissing most others.

I was resigned that it would *always* be like this.

Almost every woman on my mother's side in my family had it this bad, if not worse. Women withdrawing from the world, retreating to their solitude – their suffering – for days on end until it passed.

Pain-killers wouldn't work, my mum said. It just makes your flow weird.

(It must be true.)

Doctors won't either. They'd once wanted to put her on some *pill*. But you don't want those things in your body. They'll mess up your system. She didn't want that. Not for her, not for me.

(That must be true too.)

So pain it was.

(Not like we had a choice.)

I always wondered if that was the reason why I was so 'dramatic' during my period. That was the word they used for it: *dramatic*. And *OA*, too. Over-acting. Taking things way out of proportion and stirring trouble. Making things harder for others. Making things harder for myself.

It was my period causing it, they told me.

The *hormones*, I told myself.

I still say that to myself, when I don't eat for a day or don't leave my room for three. When I keep looking at the mirror, prodding my increasingly puffy cheeks and pinching my pillowy arms.

My period must be coming. That's why I'm thinking this.

It'll go away when it goes away.

ii.

Every child who grew up in the Philippines knows María Clara, the 'ill-starred' woman from Dr José Rizal's *Noli Me Tangere*. I guess you could say she is our Bertha Mason, although rather than being just the madwoman in the attic with no real past or context, Rizal shows you María Clara as the innocent, then the victim, then the wronged, then the mad, and finally, the lost. An epilogue. No one to reclaim her.

She was the love of the lead character Crisostomo Ibarra's life. The woman he held as a standard for all others. She was the future he strived for, the prize he was later denied for his transgressions against the Catholic Church. For the love of her, the heartbreak of losing her, and the desire to save her, he started a revolution. In María Clara, Rizal created the woman worth burning down the world for.

Why?

She was a renowned beauty with delicate features and downcast, expressive eyes; they were often compared to those of the Virgin. She was soft-spoken and gentle-natured. She was a devout Catholic, a dutiful daughter. Rizal wrote her with the idea of holding her as the epitome of Filipino womanly virtue – the dalagang Pilipina personified.

This was, of course, despite her tragic end. An end she had no hand in. Everything that María Clara suffered had been because of decisions made for her, situations where she had no agency. She could not act, could not speak. And even when she did – when she could – it was always in the throes of despair. No one really listened to her. They pitied her. They dismissed her. They ignored her. That was her fate despite the pedestal she was put on.

iii.

I started taking the Pill for the reason girls in their mid-twenties usually take the Pill.

To be an adult.

To be responsible.

I resisted it at first. But the alternatives scared me.

Injections.

Implants.

Insertions.

They all seemed so invasive. So alien.

The Pill sounded easy. Take one every day and you'll be okay.

I took it for the first time six years ago and I've mostly been on it since. Not for any other reason than it just made the pain go away.

I can still remember it, my first 'period' after taking the Pill. It was so light, so effortless. I kept running back to the bathroom just to check that I was still bleeding because it didn't feel like it. My body wasn't burning. I didn't want to just curl up in bed and sleep the next 4–6 days away.

It was still inconvenient. There wasn't much, but it was still there. You still had to change your pad or tampon every now and then. Still had the faint smell of blood around you.

But it wasn't a *real* period. The literature is quick to remind you of that. It's a *period-type* bleed.

So I took the packs back to back. I wanted to have my period as seldom as I could get away with. Two was the most I could get at the time, so I did it and I was glad. Two months straight without experiencing a period.

It was one less worry.

One less thing to make me anxious and afraid.

I felt free.

The first time I came off it was the first time I went home for Christmas after moving to Scotland.

I didn't want anyone knowing that I was taking the Pill.

(I didn't want *my mum* knowing I was taking the Pill.)

It was only going to be two weeks – one period – then I could go back to taking it like normal. None of the literature had mentioned any adverse effects. It was safe. I'd be safe.

But so much changed in those two weeks. I didn't just come home for Christmas; I came to mourn with my family after my grandfather had died a couple of weeks prior. He was the grandfather I took care of when he was diagnosed with cancer. The grandfather I lived with in the hospital as he got chemo. The grandfather I wouldn't have left if he hadn't started getting better. The grandfather I regretted leaving when they said he'd started getting worse again. The grandfather who died on his birthday, who didn't want a fussy wake and wanted to be taken to the crematorium as soon as possible. The grandfather I never got to say goodbye to.

All that in a matter of weeks.

I cried every night. At home, I cried in private because it wouldn't be right to be so upset in company.

When I came back to Scotland, I cried in private still. It wouldn't be right to burden anyone else with my personal issues.

(I didn't know how much of it was grief or the hormones.)

I spent days in my room.

Crying.

Not crying.

Being quiet so no one knew I was there.

Pretending that I was out.

Not even going to the kitchen to eat.

Only leaving my room late at night when everyone else was asleep and my takeaway had arrived.

Eating the unrefrigerated leftovers the next day.

And those were the days that I did eat. Sometimes, even a takeaway was too much.

When uni started again, I just buried myself in essays and dissertations.

When uni was over, I buried myself in drinking with friends.

When I got a job, I buried myself in work.

I learned what panic attacks were because I started having them more often.

I'd had them when I was younger but I didn't know how to explain them. I didn't need to explain them. I just knew that they were bad and that I didn't want them to happen.

But now that I was older, I felt a pressing need to find out what was going on.

More often than not, it would just be waking up in the middle of the night gasping for air, crying.

Or I wouldn't be able to sleep. I'd just stay up, wide-eyed, in the middle of the night. Tossing. Turning. Breath quickening. My heart tightening, racing in my chest. It crumbled into a ball and rammed itself again and again, as if it wanted to break a door down. I'd feel the need to weigh it down. Using both my hands to press my chest, put as much pressure on it as I could. Force it back in.

Panic attacks.

Fight or flight.

But nothing seemed to be attacking me.

Nothing had changed.

iv.

Filipino scholars agree that María Clara was one of the greatest misfortunes to ever befall the Filipino woman. For hundreds of years we were told to aspire to her. But today, she is the stereotype we struggle all our lives to defy. To my generation, she has become a cautionary tale, a poison chalice.

Patay na tuod si María Clara! people would quote, chastising any seeming adherence to an outdated model.

My mother's generation was the first to scream this. The battle cry of Gabriela – the Filipino women's liberation movement.

My mother was outspoken, independent. She was beautiful, intelligent, capable, and adaptable – and best of all, she knew all this.

Before she met my father, she'd already made peace with the possibility of being an old maid – because an unattached woman in her late twenties was still seen as such. It didn't seem like such a horrible future to her; after all, and in her own words, 'There was nothing out there that a man could offer me that I didn't already have or couldn't get for myself'. Her blueprint for a fulfilling unmarried life was a house in the countryside, animals to take care of, and countless nieces and nephews to spoil.

She raised me in the same vein. To be outspoken and independent; to know that I was beautiful, intelligent, capable and adaptable.

But María Clara's ghost was ever-present.

She may no longer be the ideal – but she is the shadow.

The haunting.

The spectre.

v.

Ang payat mo na! they said when I came home next. You've gotten so skinny!

What did I do? Did I go on a diet? Less carbs? No rice? Did I start exercising more? Whatever it was, it's working. I look amazing.

No one had ever cared about how I looked like before. I'd always been unremarkable. A good middle.

Maybe I was wrong.

(Was it the Pill?)

After two months at home – the Pill on pause – I started taking them again. Two packs back to back, one period instead of two. But things weren't the same.

It hurt again. Not as much as before, but definitely worse since I'd started taking it.

I started looking in the mirror again. My face looked so round. My belly so bloated.

I started crying more, being upset more

…worse.

The panic attacks…they seemed to grow at the same rate that I did.

At its worst, I had them at least once a month.

One had me crying on a night out. I still don't know how it started. But I had to be taken home. Had to be calmed down.

Another saw me scared that someone was going to hurt me. My loved ones had to take turns watching over me. They didn't want to leave me alone. They didn't know what would happen to me if I was left alone.

All the while I could see clothes getting tighter on me.

They didn't look the same.

They didn't feel the same.

I didn't look the same.

I didn't feel the same.

I decided that maybe I should keep taking the Pill the next time I went home. I didn't want a normal period. I didn't want to be in pain.

I told my mum.

'Did they put you on them for your period?' she asked.

'Yes', I replied, leaving out that I had sought them out.

'Just be careful. They can mess with your system'.

The hormones.

On and off, taking and not.

Was that what was causing all this? I'd considered it before, yes, but hearing my mum say it made it seem true.

Mood swings, the side effects listed. Weight gain, that wasn't listed but almost everybody said so. Friends, acquaintances, thousands of people who posted online.

It must be that, then.

It made sense.

When I got back to Scotland, I went to my GP.

The Pill shouldn't be doing that, they said. It is safe. There is no evidence that it makes women put on weight. Was I sure that it wasn't the oral steroids? I'd been on a course recently for my asthma. It must be that. And as for the mood swings…

…a trail.

Mood swings or depression?

(Yes.)

Nervousness, anxiety, and irritability?

(Yes.)

Difficulty sleeping?

(Yes.)

Lethargy?

(Yes.)

It could…I'd have to test but there could be something wrong with my thyroid.

Relief. That was what I felt. An overwhelming wave of relief. That must be it. My thyroid. Didn't my mum once say that an aunt had tested positive for hyperthyroidism? Or was it hypothyroidism? One of those. It was why she'd gained weight. It was why she was always on those diets. Like the one where she went on a lemon juice and cayenne cleanse. Or when she decided to take those supplements. It was to counteract the weight gain from the problems with her thyroid function.

(Why didn't she take the medicine? They do give out medicine to treat thyroid conditions. That's what the doctor said would happen if I tested positive.)

It made sense. It felt true. The tests hadn't even been scheduled but they already felt like the answer.

Then…

the results came back.

Nothing seemed out of the ordinary.

(No.)

Everything seemed to be in order.

(No.)

My thyroid function was perfect.

(No.)

I told my mum the results and she was happy that everything came back normal.

It must just be the hormones I'm taking.

Between…

…the inhalers

…the oral steroids

…*the Pill*

…~~hypothyroidism~~

…~~hyperthyroidism~~

…my period

it could be anything.

They account for so many things:

Digestive issues. Appetite issues. Self-esteem issues. Weight loss. Weight gain. Depression. Anxiety. Despondency. Bad mood. Mood swings. Lack of focus. Lack of sleep. Lack of anything to say.

(This was all *their* fault).

It had to be.

It had to be something chemical…biological…medical… hormonal.

It couldn't be my fault, their fault, someone else's fault.

It wasn't something I did, they did, someone else did.

It had to be *them*. Hormones.

That's right, it has to be. It can't be anything else.

It had to be *anything* else.

It can't be just *me*.

But, wouldn't it be better if it was?

The reason.

The relief.

The weight off my shoulders.

(Then maybe it could be fixed.

I could be fixed.)

vi.

'The convent for me or the grave!' María Clara cried, but it was not really her choice.

Those were the only choices they'd allowed her. With her lover disgraced, the tragedy of her parentage revealed, she had nothing left. They'd left nothing else for her.

The *Noli Me Tangere's* epilogue showed that she'd wasted away in the nunnery – descending into madness as Rizal liked to put it. A madwoman in a torn, wet gown, filled with tears and horror. That is how we last see her. A woman who watched as the gates of Heaven closed on her.

But despite all of this, we were still meant to aspire to her, emulate her.

Why?

I think it was María Clara's lack of choice – her lack of

agency – that cemented her pedestal as the Filipino ideal. Nothing was ever her fault. It was always something else. Her lover. Her father. Society. The nuns' disdain. The government official's wilful ignorance. None of it was her doing.

María Clara herself remained faultless. Like the Virgin she was often compared to, she remained pure of corruption, of sin.

And though she is dead, though we killed María Clara so that we may live the life she was never free to have, we are still haunted by her spectre.

We are no longer expected to be beautiful and elegant, remain pinnacles of grace and silent suffering – but we are still expected to remain pure of blame. Our misfortunes cannot be of our own making. Our shortcomings cannot be of our own design.

She did everything right. Nothing was ever her fault. Everyone loved her.

Yet she still died.

For them. Because of them. By their hands. By our hands. We still killed her.

Not Rizal.

Not Ibarra.

Not the *Noli*.

Her.

She was innocent. She constantly lived for the happiness of others.

And yet she deserved this?

(Maybe we were wrong to kill her.

Maybe we just needed to find her peace.)

Pangwakas na Bahagi

In English you call it a 'period' – a stretch of time. Something that comes and goes. That begins and ends.

In Filipino we say 'meron', *to have*.

(…but by the same token, *to have not*.)

It is something we have…

…something we don't.

(…something we lose.)

What next?

- **Saheliya** (*www.saheliya.co.uk*) – Saheliya is a specialist mental health and wellbeing support organisation for black, minority ethnic, asylum seeker, refugee, and migrant women and girls (12+) in the Edinburgh and Glasgow area.

dear lexi

by Tomiwa Folorunso

DEAR LEXI,

I'm sorry.

Even though so much time has passed, I keep thinking about that day and how I was and how I know I made you feel. This is your long overdue apology and, although I know you would never ask for one, an explanation.

Remember the day we drove to Chicago? Summer 2019. I say 'we' but it was all you; you did the driving. I just chose the music and hoped you wouldn't notice as I turned the air con up and kept one eye on the sat nav because, well, because we know what you're like with directions. By the time we were driving across the Chicago Skyway Toll Bridge we had covered almost 892 miles in one day. We were nothing short of delirious, which is the only acceptable explanation for listening and singing along to the Backstreet Boys. We were shrieking like children at the Fourth of July fireworks going off, convinced that they were going to hit the car and our long-awaited weekend trip would come to a very sudden, unpleasant end. I don't know about you, but as we drove through those streets flanked by Chicago's famous skyscrapers and pulled up in front of our hotel, I had butterflies in my tummy at the thought of finally being released from the car we had just spent 16 hours in. That's a long time. As we were scrambling to get our bags out of the back seat and give the car keys to the concierge, you snapped at me. A harmless snap in a stressful moment at the end of a day I could barely remember beginning. I don't remember what you said, and it doesn't actually matter. Usually, I would have responded with an eyeroll or a catty comment back, but that night I didn't. My period was due in seven days. Your tone knocked me back and something in me that I still don't really know how to explain grabbed on to that split second of hurt and ran with it. So as we checked in, collapsed onto the bed and ordered celebratory glasses of prosecco, I was so aware that I was going through the motions, performing; my smile couldn't reach my eyes, the words coming out of my mouth were landing flat, it's like not feeling anything but feeling everything at the same time. It wasn't about you anymore; it became me trying to sort out the thoughts that were filling my head and taking over my body. Irrational thoughts that are mine, thoughts that belong to me but I don't want.

It's so difficult to explain, Lex. It is me, but an off-balance me, I suppose that's what it is, isn't it? An endocrine disorder, a hormonal imbalance.

I

me

Tomiwa Folorunso

I am imbalanced.

Every month it feels as if I am losing my mind, a state of flux where you know all is not lost, yet, but you do not know how to keep what you have, scared that if you hold on too tightly you'll break it.

It's called PMDD or Premenstrual Dysphoric Disorder.

I can't remember if I told you, which makes me think I did not. I'm getting better at talking about it, explaining it, but even then, it's hard. I just describe it as *'really bad PMS'*.

I first noticed it after we finished uni. I was tired, almost falling asleep on the bus into town for work or having a 10am sofa nap. I felt more anxious than normal, and was irritable. Little things would tick me off and I felt a bit overwhelmed sometimes or struggled to concentrate. But it was a period of transition – I missed my friends, I had started a new job and moved back into my family home. There was a lot going on. I remember saying to my manager, *'I don't feel right'* and she asked me, *'Is it your time of the month?'* I shrugged my shoulders and rolled my eyes, because my PMS wasn't like that. Maybe a bit of back pain and crying when someone gave birth on TV was the extent of it. I had never been that person before.

Until then.

I can't remember the words that were said that got me there. There, as in 22 years old, staring at a reflection that I didn't recognise. A mess of tears and snot, defeated limbs and bloodshot eyes. People say that all the time, '*I couldn't recognise myself*'. But to actually stand, looking into your own eyes and not see yourself? Terrifying. I looked so broken, but inside so angry, I could feel it bubbling up inside me and I had this urge to hit something or break something, anything, to get it out of me. I picked up my cup, the one I got from the Guinness Factory with Alice, it said, 'Black is best', and I threw it at the wall. It landed on my bed. I didn't feel better. I picked it up again and threw it harder, with more force; this time it landed on the floor and rolled; the plastic straw that had come with the cup was broken, ruined.

Jumper jacket trainers headphones keys door. Down the stairs two at a time. Fresh air on my forehead. My feet tripped over themselves as if the further away I got from the scene of the crime, the better I would feel. I sat on my bench facing Fife and the lighthouse, hood up, one leg up, right cheek resting on my knee. I closed my eyes, tears fell, I just wanted someone to stroke the side of my face and tell me it's going to be okay and that I would be okay.

That was the moment '*I'm not feeling right*' became *I am not right*. That was not me. You know me, Lex, I'm a lot of things; excited, passionate, enthusiastic, a gaggle of limbs that often bumps into things. But aggressive? Violent? Angry?

Not until then.

Until now.

I searched, tracked and wrote down my symptoms.

Panic attack in the sandwich shop, crying often, craving all the food but unable to make a decision so returning from the shop with an assortment of ingredients that could make many meals but not one I could eat right then, low energy, can't get a grasp on things spiralling can't focus on work can't focus on anything numbness, despair, tired but can't sleep, I don't care I do care crying. Help. Crying. Tired of crying, tired of being tired of crying. When will this end?

I went to the doctor, prepared, because they have a habit of not believing people like me. I got a diagnosis, but a diagnosis is not a cure. I needed more than the prescription they handed to me at the end of my ten-minute appointment. A prescription for medication that I stopped taking after three months because it felt too risky. I ripped up the repeat slip and left the tablets to expire in a bedside drawer.

I could not, I will not risk losing any more of myself.

So, here I am. It used to be the actual period that I dreaded, now it's the ten to 14 days before. And when my period comes, I want to cheer, because it means I'm almost out of this dark hell hole. Then I spend the next 13 to 17 days picking up the pieces of the damage I've done and at the same time trying to find ways to break the cycle. It feels like self-sabotage.

All the usual PMS stuff I can cope with, because that's what us people who have periods have been told to do since the beginning of time.

We cope.

We cope and we tolerate, and we don't complain about the bloating, the breakouts, the tender breasts, the greasy hair, the mood swings, or the decreased sex drive.

We do not complain because the way we learnt it, the way we were taught it, this is just how it is. The reward, the light at the end of the tunnel, the pot of gold at the end of the rainbow, we are told, is being able to have children. If you can, if you can't, if you don't, if you want to, there are many different ways to have children. Even if there weren't, what kind of trade-off is that? Feel like shit every single month and then maybe if you are lucky, you get the apparent greatest gift of all, life. Biological life.

Anger, through most of the month, not just some of it.

Angry with my doctor who couldn't really tell me why this PMDD chose me and why it chose me now. Angry with a system and a lack of research that offers such limited treatment options that have me up until 3am making Venn diagrams of the side effects, only to find that it's about the lesser of two evils because when have we ever been able to have it all?

Angry with my body.

It let me down. Just when I had it all figured out, when my mental health was really getting better. The body I had worked so hard to love, to respect, to understand, and not feel ashamed of. To proudly call mine. My body.

I hate that I have to work so hard and don't understand it, that I never get a month off and every single time it is a little bit different. The physical symptoms I can manage; cramps, bloating, joint or muscle pain. Even the panic attacks, the mood swings, crying at random songs. I don't give myself a hard time for indulging my food cravings or when I have to have a lie in because I'm so tired. I don't beat myself up after a social situation where I have not been my 'best self' in energy and personality or when I slip out a little early. I just do what I need to do and stay in my safe places. But the lasting irritability, the anger, the way one harmless moment does somersaults in my head and irrationally spirals, making me lash out at the people I love and care about the most. I can't do that. That scares me. Chicago wasn't the first time, Lex, and it was not the last either. It is the one I remember the most. We are at a time in our lives where we have chosen this friendship and if you choose something, you can un-choose it. The thought of you un-choosing me – and I know you wouldn't, but you could, you might.

I had to write this down and tell you properly, because each time I go through my camera roll, I find this photo of us on top of a tour bus on that first morning in Chicago. We're a little bit sweaty, I'm wearing a white t-shirt and you've got a stripy black one, both with a pair of sunglasses, I'm smiling, and you look so unimpressed. It sums us right up and I love it so much, but hate it as well. I had hardly said any words to you that day, I couldn't be present in that moment with you because I was trying to deal with what was going on in my head, calm my anxiety and get rid of the horrible mood that had taken over. But you didn't know that, because I didn't tell you. I couldn't tell you.

Lexi, I'm sorry for those first 24 hours in Chicago. I'll take you back and we can do it all again and even though I can't promise my period won't be due in seven days, I promise to tell you if it is.

I love you.

Tomiwa x

What next?

- **Vianney Leigh** (*msha.ke/statusflow.co/*) – Vianney Leigh is a life and success coach, menstrual cycle alignment expert, and host of the *Periods and Power Moves* podcast.

let's make a baby (with science)

by Erica Gillingham

WE WEREN'T EXPECTING the silence. In our 12 years together, we had never experienced such profound awkwardness as what followed after that first hormone injection. This nightly shot would trick my ovaries into producing multiple eggs in one cycle but, right now, nothing had changed except that the syringe was empty. Sitting on our sofa, sharps box at our feet, we just held each other, minds racing. Knowing my wife like I do, I know that music will always lift Alex's spirits – and right then, I needed her to smile, to laugh, more than I needed anything that might be produced from our new medical kit. So, I started a new playlist and began filling it with songs by the women of Jazz we loved – Ella Fitzgerald, Etta James, Nina Simone, Sarah Vaughan – songs we had crooned and danced to in our living room. Then I gave our playlist a name: 'Let's Make a Baby (With Science)'.

As a queer woman in my mid-thirties, I have thought a lot about the potential conception process Alex and I would need to go through to create a family, or, more specifically, to have a child or children who would be genetically related to one of us. I have wanted children since I was a young person and Alex really, really wants to be a mum. Before I proposed to her over a decade ago now, I first asked for her parents' blessing, as she had told me she wanted them nearby on the day we got engaged. At the conspicuous lunch in London's St James's Park, I asked if they had any questions after I announced the news. 'What about grandkids?' came the united reply. 'Not to worry', I said, 'we want children, too'. The question was easy to handle because we had already been thinking and talking about the prospect, individually and collectively, throughout our adult lives.

In the intervening years, we've revisited the conversation of queer baby-making with varying degrees of levity and seriousness, broaching everything from potential baby names (somehow, mostly for girls) to the citizenship rights (British and American) of any offspring we would produce. Questions like, who would carry and whose eggs would be used? (I would carry, with my eggs.) Where would the sperm come from? (A UK-based donor with brown hair, hazel eyes, and, preferably, a penchant for science.) In which country would we conceive, and in which would we give birth? (England, both.) Which course of treatment – artificial insemination, intrauterine insemination, in vitro fertilisation – would we start with? (IVF, via egg donation.) What would happen if we couldn't conceive, and what kind of support would we need? (Alex would attempt to carry a child; we'd rely on our informal support network and formal medical care.)

When we finally agreed one New Year's Day that 'this year would be the year', we believed we'd thought through every possible scenario as far as we could imagine. Once we made it through the clinic doors and agreed to our chosen starting point, though, one glaring omission in our lists of questions and answers became clear: hormones. What hormones would be required, how would they get into my body, and what would they do to it?

I am never going to be the person who sticks herself with a needle unless it is absolutely necessary. I can handle the pain of a tattoo best out of the both of us, but there are reasons why I married a woman who has wanted to practice medicine since she was old enough to speak. Given that, as a Physician Associate, Alex works with needles on a daily basis, sometimes even accessing spinal fluid for samples, we both agreed we'd play to our strengths in this scenario. Therefore, sitting in the nurse's room, it was Alex who was taught how to mix and administer the follicle stimulating hormone (or FSH; specifically, Menopur) and the hormone antagonist (for me, Cetrotride) that would be injected into my thigh (the tummy was a no-goer for me). We were given a surplus number of needles and syringes, told to pick up the prescriptions, and in four days' time start the treatment that would, hopefully, lead to a successful IVF process and a healthy pregnancy. It was the beginning of autumn, the season in which we fell in love; it seemed like a good omen.

Back in the spring, we had still been deciding where to start. We've never been a particularly private couple, so one of the friends who knew these baby-making conversations were happening suggested we get in touch with a local same-sex couple for a recommendation on a London clinic. All of our other friends who were in same-sex partnerships had either gone abroad or used a known donor, neither of which appealed to us. These women had two children through fertility treatment, and had taken part in an egg donation programme in exchange for free IVF treatment (not including the cost of sperm and the mandatory HEFA fee). With limited financial resources, this seemed like an excitingly expedient option for us: it was a treatment within our budget with a relatively high success rate and had the emotional benefits of a charitable act (akin to the one we required with sperm donation). It was a big jump for our first try, but it was at least an option worth exploring sooner rather than later, as I still had 18 months to go before the cut-off age of 36 years old.

Once I had been cleared for the egg donation programme, the first – of many, we would learn – waiting periods began: anticipating our match with the recipient. While the clinic sent off my anonymous details to a first and then a second potential recipient candidate, I started the oral contraceptive pill. This would allow the clinic to more easily sync our cycles for the treatment. I understood this intellectually, but I wasn't thrilled about it. I'd taken the Pill once before, for three months at age 19, and it was awful. It had been a somewhat arbitrary prescription for an unconfirmed ovarian (non-)issue that coincided with my first major break-up. I can safely say it was the first time I experienced depression. But this time the Pill was temporary, for less than six weeks, with a very specific purpose and a clear, desired outcome. As it happened, I ended up washing down the first pill with a glass of prosecco on a girls' weekend in Brighton and tried not to think about what other hormones we'd be adding into the mix in just a short time.

After the silence of the first injection, I was hopeful that the second night would feel a little better with our ironically saucy playlist of songs at the ready. I hit the play button to start Ella Fitzgerald crooning 'Let's Do It' and tried to relax while Alex mixed the FSH medication: one ampoule of saline and three small jars containing a tablet of powder that instantly dissolved. Next came Etta James singing 'I Just Want to Make Love to You', which I playfully lip-synced to Alex across the coffee table as she tried to keep her focus so as not to miss a single drop of liquid. But when it came time for the actual needle-to-skin part, the music just felt silly, out of place, and I started to bristle and squirm. We needed silence for this. I switched off the music, we completed the task, and then I turned in for a hug as the tears started again. It all felt so strange: so monumental and yet nothing tangible.

After a short time, Alex nudged me. 'Shall we start the music again? It's a little quiet'. She was right, it was, and we needed something to pull ourselves back from getting lost in the quagmire of *What the hell are we doing?* As soon as Sharon Jones started in on 'Let Them Knock', the world felt a little more right again. We began adding other favourites, too: Nina Simone's 'Feeling Good', Dinah Washington's 'Teach Me Tonight', Sarah Vaughan's 'They Can't Take That Away from Me'; another by Ella, this time 'It's Only a Paper Moon'. There was comfort in these songs that were performed with a wink and a nod, songs we'd sung to each other with a cheeky grin of queering the object of affection. They didn't erase the waves of anger that continued to surface, rising from the fact we needed any outside intervention at all, that we couldn't just make like Ella and say, 'Let's do it' on our own, with our two bodies. Still, we were making each decision in our own way.

By the beginning of the second week of the treatment, I wasn't yet feeling any different, physically. I still couldn't have any music on when Alex administered the drugs, but when the second medication – the hormone antagonist – was added, I got in on the at-home chemistry lesson by preparing the FSH solution, and that felt better, more active. I didn't have as much time for anxiety to build if I was trying to angle the larger gauge needle *just right* in order to get that *last little drop of saline into the syringe already!* One thing that did change, though, as the days went on and the ovarian follicles started showing their rapid growth on the scans, was that I had to stop my recently begun 'Couch to 5K' running programme. As a queer woman who came out during the original broadcast of *The L Word*, I had made like Tina and started running again, in preparation for what I hoped would be my impending pregnancy. However, when you have clusters of fluid-filled sacs that are multiple centimetres wide taking up space in your reproductive system, they don't like being jostled around, *thank you very much*. After two runs that left me queasy and with cramp-like pain, I called off the aspirational running and just focused on making my scan appointments, drinking enough water, and going to work.

I have a photocopy of the chart of my follicle growth filled in by the sonographer after each of our scans. It shows the development from little clusters of circles tightly bunched together on one corner of the graph at the beginning of the cycle to a spread of follicles in a single column, ranging in size from a millimetre to over two centimetres. There were 23 in total, which was plenty, so they scheduled the vaginal egg collection for two days after the last scan. (A brief pause to thank our sonographer, Liz, who, quite honestly, made the whole multi-week process bearable: when that person is the one consistent person in your treatment, they can mean the difference between leaving each appointment crying or feeling like you are perfectly whole, just as you are. Thank you, no-nonsense-and-yet-kind sonographers.) The surgery went well: the surgeon retrieved 13 eggs – we received seven, and our recipient received six – the sperm defrosted, and the eggs were fertilised. I responded well to everything, even if nausea was a bit of a problem later in the day, a side effect of the anaesthesia.

We received a phone call the next day to say that five eggs had fertilised but, by the sixth day, we only had two embryos (blastocysts) that had made the grade. One was frozen, and one was transferred. It was strange to place my hand on my abdomen, as we walked out of the clinic after the ten-minute procedure, and think, 'I'm carrying an embryo in my uterus'. It was a detached sense of potential: no sense of guarantee and yet a moment that could be truly life changing. We hopped in a black cab for a ten-minute ride to a favourite proper London caff, ordered a pair of fry-ups, and snuck peeks at the photograph of the embryo taken from the microscope. We were cautiously optimistic, but also didn't know any better. How are you supposed to behave when you've never done a thing before, and the doing of the thing is completely beyond the power of your control?

Thankfully, we had been warned that the next two weeks – the dreaded 'two week wait' – might be difficult. Hormonally, I was somewhere on the emotional spectrum of 'I really hope this works. Please work. Oh my god, I think it might have worked' for the first week. I had started administering progesterone suppositories to help stabilise the uterine lining and support the implantation. My body seemed to be responding to something, and we thought maybe, just maybe… Then, something shifted in my body, physically.

Two days before our first scheduled pregnancy test, it was like a switch had gone off. My breasts, which had been tender and swollen, dropped. My abdomen, which had felt taught and round, fell flat. When I went to the bathroom mid-morning, my first sign of spotting appeared. I spent the day at home on my own, per usual, writing and reading for work, with a growing sense of dread: I wasn't pregnant.

I'm not going to lie: the week that followed was awful. Seeing Alex, my beloved, in pieces broke me. I felt numb for the first few days, and then kept bursting into tears after I'd returned to work. (My colleagues sent me home: thank you.) We didn't try again with our frozen embryo until the following February and, when I pitched this essay, I thought maybe, just maybe, I'd be writing it whilst pregnant. But that embryo didn't stick around either. Now, the COVID-19 pandemic has stopped all new treatments for the foreseeable, and my body is a vessel for me alone.

We do, though, have a silver lining to hold onto through a period of so much uncertainty: Reader, we have frozen blastocysts waiting for us. In March, in a way that only hormones can do, my body expanded so many follicles, produced so many eggs, that I tipped into ovarian hyper-stimulation, on the exact same drugs as before. We didn't know until I came out of surgery, no one did. It meant we couldn't immediately transfer an embryo, and I was laid up for a week, slowly recovering from the pair of grapefruit-sized follicle clusters I'd been carrying around. All the embryos that became blastocysts were frozen, but it means I might not have to do that treatment ever again. Something we do know is that I'll need to have an additional dose of injected progesterone whenever we are able to try again, which means there's only one pressing question remaining: how long is that needle, and where does it have to go?

What next?

- *Love Song for Baby X* by Cheryl Dumesnil

the feminine chaotic

endocrine disorders, the feminine identity and queer culture

by Lj Gray

I WAS NEVER particularly good at being a girl, as I was never very girly.

I cut my hair short because it was stubborn and knotted easily. I liked it better that way and I liked when the lady at the ice-cream van called me 'son'. Hiding my girlishness felt good – it wasn't a perfect fit, but it was comfier than trying to shoehorn myself into the mould that the late nineties/early noughties created for girls. I always resonated more with Han than Leia; I wanted to be a scruffy-looking nerf herder and fly the *Millennium Falcon* with Chewie. I liked to practice professional wrestling moves with my best friend in his back garden, and I wanted to be Eddie Guerrero and hit the Frog Splash from the top rope without being told I shouldn't because it was for boys and girls shouldn't like wrestling.

When I started secondary school the pressure of being butch and not looking or acting like other girls began to weigh heavy on my mind; I didn't want to grow my hair, shave my legs, or smoke cigarettes to curb my appetite – but I did. I grew up in a small town on the west coast of Scotland, and like many small towns in North Ayrshire, my wee town had a very small-town mentality. Without the luxury of easy access to the internet, there was no way to access information about gender identity and variability, so if you had ovaries you were expected to dress and act in the uniform prescribed by the normative gender expression of the time. The othering of people who didn't observe traditional notions of femininity was vicious and wouldn't spare the likes of me: the little girl who wanted to be Eddie Guerrero and gave all her dollies a short back and sides (sorry mum).

But what is femininity? It's easy to picture, but not so easy to define.

Reductively, femininity is the performative expression of womanhood. It is often associated with delicacy and prettiness, and it is firmly rooted in compulsory heterosexuality and biological essentialism. Femininity as a concept is manmade and spans indiscriminately across cultural, social, and political lines. It defines physical attributes, abilities, and career choices, and regulates gender expression to support hegemonic masculinity. Historically, women have been portrayed as delicate, slight, and submissive homemakers, wives, and mothers. We may grow with the times and evolve with the world around us, but the underpinning of femininity stays the same as a result of gender-normative socialisation.

As performative femininity is so deeply ingrained in our society, when we fail to meet the beauty standards that accompany normative feminine expression, it can have devastating effects on our identities and worth. It particularly affects girls and young femmes – that is to say, young people who prescribe to notions of normative femininity but are not cis women. The advent of perfectly manicured influencers promoted on Instagram feeds and viral trends or challenges on TikTok have brought forth a new age of insecurities for modern femmes that no amount of body-positive hashtags can undo. I have always had a wee knot that ached in the back of my brain every time I tried to shrink my plus-sized body, broad shoulders, and large muscular legs into a smaller, more feminine shape. I was stronger and my voice was lower than my friends who were cis women. Femininity seemed to come so naturally to them, but it still felt like breaking in a pair of hard leather boots to me, and in the end I'd shave off my long hair to try to get rid of the knots.

I'd heard the name PCOS before and I knew friends who had it, but I couldn't tell you what it was if you asked me when I was diagnosed in my early twenties. I was a young cis woman and fledgling feminist; I was embracing doctrines that were a massive 'fuck you' to traditional notions of performative gender and that finally made me more comfortable and confident in my femininity. It is because of this that the year leading up to my diagnosis was so difficult for me. The changes happened slowly and then all at once; I'd always had a fuzzy face but suddenly the hair was thicker and darker than it used to be. It started popping up on my neck and chin faster than I could get rid of it and I started to notice it on my chest and stomach. I'd kept the hair on my head short, but I noticed it was becoming much thinner and falling out. I had acne for the first time in my life and I was rapidly gaining weight around my abdominal area. I was lucky to have a GP who identified PCOS even before the blood test confirmed elevated androgen levels, but coming to terms with the diagnosis was hard, and to top it all off – there is *no cure*.

Polycystic ovary syndrome is very common; however, it remains largely underdiagnosed and unmanaged in most people who have it. It is estimated to affect one in 12 people with menstrual cycles who are of reproductive age. The endocrine system is the body's chemical messaging service responsible for regulating hormones from the glands to the circulatory system. There are numerous sex hormone disorders, many of which affect our experiences with gender identity. Amenorrhea and polycystic ovary syndrome both affect the physical traits associated with normative gender expression in people with ovaries. The symptoms of PCOS are entirely at odds with the ideals of femininity and attractiveness that we are socialised to internalise – for example, the disorder causes male pattern hair loss, hirsutism, and predisposition to disproportional abdominal fat. Androgen excess may also contribute towards increasing lean muscle mass. All of these symptoms can cause gender dysphoria for femmes and women, or those who feel the weight of socialised femininity. The gendered nature of healthcare, particularly sexual healthcare, can create an additional barrier for trans and gender-nonconforming people in need of information or treatment, and endocrine disorders can be a source of serious distress for those of us who don't prescribe to our assigned genders.

For a long time I felt like I was made wrong, in some deep and unknowable way; I didn't act like a girl, I didn't believe I even looked or felt like a girl, but I didn't look or feel like a boy either. Just as I thought I had started to get a handle on my relationship with gender expression, the diagnosis of my endocrine disorder brought my old battle with femininity back into focus. Despite feminism providing me the tools to unlearn the toxicity of normative performative femininity, I was still struggling to unlearn the insecurities and hurt it had caused over the years. Over time I began to wonder if my body's excess production of androgens had an impact on my tumultuous relationship with the feminine identity. Could it be as simple as conflating masculine hormones with performative normative femininity? I armed myself with as much knowledge on PCOS as possible and journeyed out into the literary wilderness beyond Judith Butler and Jack Halberstam to find the links between the feminine identity and endocrine disorders.

As I identified as cisgender at the time, I initially focused on cis women with PCOS. Amongst many of those women who were struggling with not feeling feminine enough, there were beacons of positivity and hope. I stumbled across model and activist Harnaam Kaur – a beautiful and vibrant young woman with a full beard. She was confident and feminine, but it was her words that truly mesmerised me, as she chose to grow her beard out to buck against society's expectations of what a woman should look like. Harnaam, flanked by stunning softly lit photographs of her with flowers placed lavishly in her beard, famously writes in a 2015 article in *Rock n Roll Bride*: 'I am happy living as a young beautiful bearded woman. I have realised that this body is mine, I own it, I do not have any other body to live in so I may as well love it unconditionally'. I found more and more cis women with endocrine disorders who were comfortable in their feminine identity. Some of them embraced the physical traits associated with their disorder, others were more content investing in products and practices that enhanced their femininity to keep up with normative beauty practices, but the one thing was clear: my experiences didn't match theirs, as their androgen increase hadn't ultimately dampened their relationship with femininity. I continued to journey on, investing in two rounds of laser hair removal as I went – reader, they were unsuccessful and I ended up skint and just as confused as I had started.

All of a sudden, there was a boom in literature about transgender people. High-profile transgender celebrities were the source of the conversation on gender and sex coming into the mainstream. The discourse was (and still is) dehumanising, and trans women were subjected to the toxic beauty standards that come with socialised and internalised femininity. At this point I had grown from a fledgling baby feminist into a full-blown feminist killjoy, and I aligned myself firmly in the intersectional camp. Gender identity became a tenet of my feminism and my career as a legal professional; I applied gender-focused feminist jurisprudence to my theory and practice. But there is a lot about gender studies and queer theory that cannot simply be learned through academic means, but through lived experience. I had already immersed myself into a flourishing community of trans and non-binary activists, creatives, and academics which gave me valuable insight into how my peers in the queer community personally experienced femininity and engaged with their feminine identity. People close to me had the courage to come out as transgender, non-binary, agender, and demigender; there was a galaxy of gender identities that I never knew existed, and suddenly things were clearer.

Femininity isn't exclusive to women.

Femininity is subjective.

Femininity can be queer.

Femmes can be *thems*.

Them. My relationship woes hadn't been with femininity, but instead I had been wrestling with binary gender and just didn't know it. I quietly came out as non-binary in my late twenties; it didn't hurt like breaking in a new pair of Docs, and it never knots.

Non-binary is a multi-purpose umbrella term to describe those who identify as a gender outside of the gender binary (male or female). Though gender-nonconforming people are often associated with androgyny, I found myself more comfortable in my feminine identity after coming out. I have often wondered if the excess of androgens as the result of my PCOS has affected my gender identity since my days of chasing the ice-cream van and wanting to be Eddie Guerrero when I grew up. Though there has been some research into transmascs and trans men who have PCOS, there has been little, if any, research on endocrine disorders and gender-nonconforming people.

Femininity as a concept is not unique to cis women; the physical traits that accompany the concept can be chopped and changed to fit anyone. It is entirely subjective and shouldn't be tied to compulsory heterosexuality. Femininity as a concept is no longer manmade. It has been reclaimed by queer culture to represent femmes everywhere, whether that is a beautiful cis woman with a full beard, a gorgeous trans woman, or a wee non-binary person who lives in Dundee and likes wrestling and ice cream.

What next?

- **The Vagina Museum** (*vaginamuseum.co.uk*) – The Vagina Museum aims to spread knowledge and raise awareness of gynaecological anatomy and health, as well as giving confidence to people to talk about issues surrounding gynaecological anatomy.

blood is back

how my knowledge and experience of periods were revolutionised while i wasn't having them

by Rachel Grocott

I STARTED FREELANCING for Bloody Good Period (BGP), the charity which provides period products to refugees, asylum seekers, and those who can't afford them, when I was six months pregnant – so I had already been period-free for half a year. My periods returned when my son was just over a year old, meaning that for a good 18 months, while I was busily scheduling menstrual-themed art, writing period-related captions and reading every bleeding-related news piece around, I wasn't actually having them myself. And when they did come back, they found me a rather different person to the one who had tentatively started writing about all things bloody, all those months before.

Like many people, I used to see periods as a complete pain, practically and literally. I certainly never thought much about the products I used, only whether I had enough (and how much chocolate to buy alongside my 'feminine hygiene' supplies – more on that naming convention later). I only had a vague concept of the problem of period poverty. Now I understand more of its reality, its prevalence, and its impact, particularly on refugees and asylum seekers – people who've already suffered indescribable trauma. It affects others too, of course: schoolgirls, the homeless, people affected by austerity – basically, anyone who can't afford or access period supplies in this crazy world which allows big companies to make big money out of a biological function. Now I understand that to not have to worry about my period means that I have a very particular kind of privilege.

Research by Plan UK has shown that one in ten girls in the UK have been unable to afford period supplies.[1] The issue of affordability is amplified for people living in any kind of vulnerable situation, including asylum seekers, who receive just £37.75 per week to live on, and (contrary to what many mainstream media outlets would have you believe) are generally not allowed to work. A heavy period can cost a quarter of that allowance, and the trauma of displacement (and possibly far more) means that this group is even more likely to suffer from irregular and heavy bleeding. As Marie, an asylum-seeking woman based in Birmingham, told BGP: 'The stress of destitution changed my menstruation cycle. I was so worried about where we would eat, what would happen, I began bleeding more often'.

Gabby Edlin, BGP's founder and CEO, started Bloody Good Period when she realised that drop-in centres (organisations offering a safe, welcoming, and supportive environment for refugees and asylum seekers, and practical support including food and other supplies) had simply not factored in menstruation. Most were not routinely giving out supplies, either at the frequency required or at all – that is, every single bloody month. So she set about collecting pads, and the rest is history. We are now partnered with 50 drop-ins across the country, giving out over 1,500 products per month. We estimate to have taken care of 60,000 periods.

This is a bittersweet set of figures. Whilst it is amazing that we can offer this support to people who would otherwise be unlikely to access these most basic of products, we shouldn't have to. We shouldn't have to rely on an act of charity for people to be able to manage their bleeding. We shouldn't have to encourage people to donate products by describing how other humans would otherwise have to use socks, newspaper, loo roll, or nothing at all.

We also passionately believe that this isn't just about giving out free products. For the past year, we have been piloting our education programme, getting vital menstrual and reproductive health information to the people we work with who, again, would otherwise be unlikely to access it. This is the kind of information we should all have access to, but most people have never had a comprehensive education about periods. Instead, we've had advertising campaigns aimed at making bleeding feel dirty. 'Freshen up with our pads', says this big corporation, 'use our rustle-free wrapper', shouts another. No wonder most societies have an impressive number of euphemisms for periods, everything from 'shark week' to 'Aunt Flo', and probably a load more you've never heard of. Many people struggle to say the word itself.

At BGP we set out to tackle this head on as well. We call the pads we collect 'period products', or 'period supplies'. Or how about just 'pads'? They are not, and never will be in our book, 'sanitary' or 'feminine hygiene' products. These delightful terms co-opted by those classic marketing campaigns are just another of the many layers of shame and embarrassment over periods. As Jane Garvey brilliantly put it on the *Woman's Hour* podcast recently, you don't find a 'masculine hygiene' aisle in Boots, do you? I've now started to understand how these layers have been present in my life and nearly everyone else's, whether they have periods or not. Whether it's the boys being sent out of the room for 'the talk' at school, or comments on social media about why women can't just 'hold it in' (yes, really). The level of ignorance and stigma surrounding periods is astounding. But I just hadn't thought about it before. I was, albeit unwillingly, *complicit* in it before.

Now I display my BGP sticker-adorned laptop on the train with pride, and talk to my friends about it – it turns out they're quite happy to chat periods, too, because periods are actually pretty normal, and a widely shared experience. Having a baby, as I have recently done, is another shared experience: celebrated and rewarded, the details discussed over coffee or wine (okay, often wine), chatted about with other people in the playground, yet having periods is hushed up, seen as something disgusting, cloaked in euphemism. But the more we talk about it, the weaker the taboo becomes (to paraphrase Sally King's 'weak taboo' description of menstruation[2]). It's my hope and intention that my five-year-old daughter is never embarrassed by her body functioning healthily, yet I also know that it's easier said than done. Years of conditioning (i.e. a lifetime, and on top of that a few more generations' influence through older relatives) don't disappear overnight, and I recently had to challenge myself not to brush away my daughter's questions about why I was bleeding. She didn't overly care, as she wanted to get back to playing – always her priority – but I know my answers now will add up to important feelings about this later on.

My awareness has changed in other ways too. Whilst I knew the biological basics of what a period was before, now I realise my knowledge was pretty one-dimensional: it didn't include any understanding or questioning of how it might affect my skills, sociability, energy levels, mood, and, well, my whole life each month. Or that it's not just about the blood bit, but what happens during the rest of a menstrual cycle too. Thanks to learning about writers such as Maisie Hill through BGP, I now have a far better knowledge of what the hell is actually going on each month. I was even excited to start tracking my periods and symptoms and for once, it didn't come as one of those 'ohhhh' moments when my period started. I understood how to listen to my body. Moreover, I understand that periods are a reflection of your health – indeed, many writers (including Chris Bobel and Maisie Hill) now describe how the menstrual cycle should be considered our fifth vital sign, an indicator of an individual's health and wellbeing as much as temperature, pulse, breathing rate, and blood pressure. Understanding all of this can help you live a more informed and empowered life – something which is both fundamental and powerful. I will still be buying loads of chocolate (always), but I'll be doing other things too, like supplementing with magnesium (for cramps – it seemed to help for the first one back, which can be notoriously tricky post-baby) and actually giving myself permission to rest (shocking).

But why isn't this knowledge more readily available to everyone? Why aren't we all taught about this at school? Everyone who has periods should be able to understand what is happening, and how to work with it each month. Everyone who cares about anyone who has a period should be able to do the same, so they can understand, empathise and support. Instead, we have a society that brushes periods under our collective and metaphorical rug and worse, marginalises people who have them, and then makes money out of them on top. It's time to turn that craziness on its bloody head.

My personal experience also shows that it's not just period knowledge we need. Like many people who experience pregnancy, I rode a complete hormonal rollercoaster when my baby started reducing the amount he was breastfeeding, and my periods returned. Also, like many, I experienced anxiety and low mood, yet found that this topic is little talked about, under-researched, and too often dismissed. And that, of course, is all part and parcel of the much bigger problem of 'women's issues' being side-lined, ignored, only seen as outliers. I was just as horrified to learn that some (not all, but some) doctors still dismiss sickness in pregnancy – yet pregnancy and having children is so revered and celebrated (it's just all the messy stuff that comes with it that needs to be hidden away). Our society uses the term 'hormonal' as an apology and often as an insult too, and that's another heap of craziness that needs to be turned around.

I fully recognise, of course, that I write all of this from a place of incredible privilege. I've been fortunate enough to have access to a whole load of inspiring and empowering information through my work; but before that, despite having a privileged upbringing, I had nowhere near enough information or support, something which is true of a vast majority of menstruating people in the UK. After all, nearly half of people in the UK don't know what's happening to them when they get their first period.[3] That issue is writ large for the people with whom BGP works, and for anyone vulnerable in a society which has marginalised menstruation and the people who experience it. That urgently needs to change. The panic-buying of period products during the COVID-19 outbreak only underlines how essential period products are – but vulnerable people, including asylum seekers receiving £37.75 per week, can't bulk buy anything. Neither can they routinely access the kind of information I've described here.

That's why Bloody Good Period is not just about ending period poverty, and not just about giving out pads (as vital as that service is). We are for menstrual equity: a society in which the simple biological fact of bleeding doesn't hold anyone back from participating fully in society, or in life. Or, more simply, a society where everyone has a bloody good period.

What next?

- **Bloody Good Period** (*bloodygoodperiod.com*) – Bloody Good Period gives period products to those who can't afford them, and provides menstrual education to those less likely to be able to access it.
- ***Periods Gone Public*** by Jennifer Weiss-Wolf

my anxiety is part of my identity

by Toonika Guha

THE YEAR WAS 2016. It was a hot summer day, with barely any air in my small London studio. I was lying on top of all my covers, trying to catch my breath. It had been a few minutes, but I couldn't seem to steady my breathing.

I was due to go to Edinburgh for a summit for students in the Arts the following week, but how would I go? I hadn't left my apartment in days, save for short runs to Sainsbury's to buy sustenance; I rarely had a day when I got out of bed without difficulty.

The following Sunday, the residence put out a large breakfast spread for those of us who were too caught up with dissertation work to make food. I was one of those students. But I was caught up with my anxiety, rather than my dissertation. I had somehow managed to finish the bulk of it before my anxiety caught up with me. I felt that I must get out of bed, go down to the courtyard and stuff my face with pancakes and waffles. I *needed* the food, I *craved* the company. But when the day arrived, I could barely sit up in bed. Hunger got the better of me in the end. I crawled out in my hoodie and pyjamas and made my way to the courtyard, where most other students were smartly dressed for the cool morning. The feast was largely over, but I managed to fill my stomach with sweet sandwiches and waffles. I had eaten around other people. I was still breathing. I had gotten out of bed. It was a victory.

I have had anxiety for as long as my mind can remember. Perhaps I have lived with the condition long before it was understood or identified, but it was properly diagnosed around the time I was studying abroad. I have always had a lot of noise in my head, sometimes pushing me to work harder and sometimes clouding my judgement, but the first time that it got cloudy enough for me to take note was the year that I turned 22.

How does one talk about the experience? How does one successfully express oneself when one's head is too full of noise and static? Well, one doesn't. Not easily at least. Ever since I've realised the nature of my condition, I have struggled to write or talk about it on public platforms for many reasons. Firstly, while the anxiety has been a constant, how it makes me feel shifts and changes quite a bit. There is very little constant to talk about. Secondly, talking about a health issue comes with its own set of stigmas. This is why, for the longest time, I never spoke about my mental health in a work space. It is very easy (for those who are so inclined) to use evidence of your mental ill-health to discredit you in any scenario, especially in a work-related one. While there has been an opening up of safe spaces for conversations on mental health, for someone who lives with an issue on a daily basis, it is scary to come out and talk about it. But the more I remain silent, the more it will force hundreds like me to remain silent. So this is me, coming out and talking about mental health, anxiety, therapy, medication, identity, and everything in between.

Ankita (name changed to protect identity) was the fourth therapist that I saw. The first one I had met about three years before in London, and they understood me very little. It was my first experience with therapy and I soon gave up on it, although the sensation of anxiety in my head was quite debilitating. I decided that it would be easier for me to live through my anxiety than expose myself to a massive cultural difference and lack of comprehension with this therapist in a foreign country. I met my second therapist when I moved back to my hometown in Kolkata. I'm not sure what her methods were, but I swear I thought she would fall asleep during our sessions. She would occasionally nod and rarely ask questions while I rambled away, without reaching any conclusions. My experiences with these two ladies were so devastating that I just couldn't bring myself to get help at all after that. Not only did their sessions not help, but their lack of diagnosis made me feel that my condition was imagined. My third therapist was a bright young lady in Delhi who was the first person to help me see some light. She used psychotherapy to help train my mind to find its way out of the mist, making me feel like a functional person. But for some reason, after a year of seeing her, she seemed to disappear – not taking my calls or appointments. And that was that in terms of our relationship.

By the time I met Ankita, I was not only a ball of anxiety, but had also lost a lot of faith in the therapeutic process. But my anxiety had gotten progressively worse, so I decided that I couldn't continue without help. Ankita suggested that I supplement my therapy with hormonal medication. She believed that in my condition, having lived with anxiety for as long as I had, it would be difficult to restore normalcy without the help of medication. After three failed attempts with therapists I had become sceptical of the process, but I was desperate to feel better. So feeling quite defeated, I gave in to the chemical treatment.

I started off with the smallest dosage of anti-anxiety medication. It was also during this time that I was diagnosed with deficiencies of iron, vitamin D, and B12 – all of which were contributing to my anxiety. Needless to say, I was put on supplements for all of these things. My medication was finally keeping me 'sane' and it was the best thing to have happened to my mental health in a while.

It is important to note that perhaps the medication alone may not have worked so well if it wasn't supplemented with rigorous weekly sessions of therapy. Apart from the fact that my first two therapists were unable to help me, perhaps the third couldn't go all the way with my healing because of the lack of medication. I learnt that with the kind of anxiety that I was battling, medication and therapy went hand in hand on the road to healing. While being in weekly sessions helped me stay in a controlled environment where I worked on problem-solving mechanisms for my anxiety, the medication helped balance the serotonin levels in my head, helping them come to 'normal' levels.

By February of 2020, I was feeling close to what one can define as 'normal'. I wasn't having any anxiety attacks, I was travelling across the country to deliver work sessions, I managed to fit in two cross-country wedding invitations, while having a group of my friends stay over with me. My anxiety felt like it was nearly gone, and I decided that it was time for me to renegotiate my identity. One of my first concerns about actually getting better was that I wouldn't know who I would be without it. It had become such an intrinsic part of my identity that I felt like I wouldn't know how to function anxiety-free. For the three years that I had had aggravated anxiety, every thought, every action was governed and ruled by the anxiety in my head. I would choose my actions each day based on how my anxiety was doing, and rarely was there a time when I was able to surmount it to make conscious choices that were not tinged by this nagging feeling in my head. But come February 2020, that was all about to change. I negotiated conversations at work without my anxiety; I picked out clothes for my friends' weddings without anxiety; I took late night and early morning flights without anxiety – my life was finally about to change. I would be a new person.

While I was elated to finally be able to not overthink things, in the back of my head, I started to wonder who I would be without this force pushing me harder and harder – sometimes to the extent that I was immobilised.

I was 14 when I started researching colleges and admission processes. While my friends went out and got themselves boyfriends and makeup, my nagging anxiety (quite mild at that time) pushed me to look for better options for myself so that I could get ahead in life. This was the good thing about my anxiety. It made me active, it made me do things. But as I mentioned, by the time I turned 22, it had turned into a monster in my head that pushed me so hard and made me worry so much that I could barely get out of bed, to beat the feeling of being overwhelmed. So while I did spend three years, four therapists, lots of money, and medication on making myself better, I felt a deep sense of loss as my anxiety wore out.

Ankita asked me to slow down a little and said it was a good thing that I wasn't propelled by fear in life, but I wasn't so sure. I feared that I would have to rebuild a fundamental part of my identity and replace my anxiety with something else.

With the fog of anxiety nearly gone by mid-February, I began to notice that it was replaced by a different sensation – that of anger. In the absence of the fog around my thoughts, I could, for the first time in a long while, see people and actions around me for what they were – I realised that I was acting towards them with anger rather than understanding, rationale, and compassion, as had been my MO previously. Was I a naturally angry person? Had my anxiety been hiding a bubbling and angry mind for so long?

It turns out that was not that case. As it appears, one of the hormonal medications that I had been taking was affecting my brain in such a way that it was making me an angry person – something that was completely out of character. But the benefit of being in a medical programme in a closely monitored environment is that your therapist takes note of the slightest behavioural changes. I was immediately diagnosed, my medication adjusted, and I was on my way to getting better. Or so I thought.

It was mid-March when the coronavirus pandemic hit India fully. Offices started to shut down as the country prepared to go into lockdown. At this time, my mental health was well and truly better, as I was on the lowest dose of medication and feeling quite functional. But I was barely out of the woods.

A couple of weeks in, social isolation at home really started to get to me. My body went into survival mode, and my anxiety started to spike. I started having frequent panic attacks where I couldn't breathe properly for up to ten minutes at a time. My doctors decided that it was time to up my medication, with the option of an SOS dose at hand. Knowing that they were there for me was reassuring, but I didn't get any better. In fact, I started sleeping more and more until all I was doing was eating and sleeping, with little energy to do anything else.

This was followed by three rounds of adjusting and readjusting medication. I like to compare the administering of mental health medication to adjusting salt in a cooking dish. While there is no real-time test one can perform to understand the balance of hormones, it is a matter of adjusting and readjusting the levels until one stabilises.

At the end of three rounds of medication adjustments, my doctors and I realised that while I was less anxious, my medications were slowing me down and making me sluggish. Maybe the anxiety is just a part of who I am, they wondered.

I wonder the same thing. While it evolved into something truly menacing in my twenties, my anxiety has been a constant companion in my head throughout my life. And maybe the goal shouldn't be to banish it. Maybe it is for me to learn to control it, with the help of both medication and therapy. Maybe it isn't a demon that needs to be defeated, but a spirit that I need to tame as part of my personality to help me reach my goals.

What next?

- **The Live Love Laugh Foundation**
  (thelivelovelaughfoundation.org) – Founded by Deepika Padukone, TLLLF aims to give hope to every person experiencing stress, anxiety, and depression. Their programmes encompass mental health awareness and de-stigmatisation.

wanna see my party trick? *stops taking t*

by James Hudson

THE DUBLIN FRINGE Festival started a month after I finished college, and as a jobless graduate with not one but two unmarketable arts degrees, I decided I might as well volunteer.

The festival led me to a queer club night, where I met a beautiful person without a gender. Their hair was natural black and a grungy garage band length, and they could tie the fringe back in a way that made every stray, choppy curl fall with purpose. They told me they wanted to grow it out like Kurt Cobain. For years I had been showing the hairdresser pictures of Jean Seberg from a Google search of 'girls with boys' hair'.

I thought of the age-old gay dilemma: *do I want to be them, or be with them?*

Sometime later the boy committed to a mullet. Their mane was reined in and my greatest obstacle at the time – blatantly copycatting someone I found attractive – disappeared.

I decided to grow my own hair out. And I thought: *maybe I should start taking testosterone again.*

Back in my undergrad, I had avoided four monthly hormone injections before I started telling people I was 'taking a break from T'.

The mood swings, the skin problems, the doctor's fees, you know, I vamped, when no one had asked me to. I really was run ragged in college, but to this day I couldn't tell you how much of that was the testosterone's fault.

I was in University College Dublin and surrounded by arts students at the time. Everyone was well clued in to trans topics from their lefty upbringings and childhoods scrolling Tumblr, which I can say because I did it too. Despite my feminine features, the arts block had gendered me correctly from the minute I introduced myself as 'James'. They continued to do so well after I started mentioning that I had stopped taking T, for all my given reasons.

I can't remember any context in which I could have brought this up organically, but I managed to inform everyone from long-time family friends to one-off acquaintances that I had decided to stop taking testosterone. Who knows what they made of that – was this a cause for celebration? Gross oversharing? A damning condemnation of millennial transtrenders? Whatever they thought, everyone gave me the same reaction; they acknowledged the fact and moved on, like it hadn't concerned them in the first place.

I found weaker and weaker reasons to bring up the subject and opened up more with each conversation, blabbing about increasingly vulnerable subjects with diminishing returns. After the relief of being accepted by someone, oestrogen and all, I still brought up hormones with the next person, hoping they'd be the one to finally ask me for just one more word on the subject. I don't know what I would have said if they had asked me to tell them more about my life off T. I might have had the chance to hear myself say that I was not just less sad, but happier now. I might have thought about that more before I decided to grow my hair out.

The arts block was sound, my mother was loving, my friends outside university showed unwavering support, and I didn't feel pressure to 'pass' for anyone. There were people in my life I could lean on and whine that my period was killing me this month. I didn't wear a chest binder around them. And they would never hold those things against me.

I could easily live without taking testosterone until college was over.

College was over.

It had been over for months, and there had been no jabs of hormones to the muscle of my thigh.

By the time I graduated from UCD, my mind was feeling the lightest it had since I was a child. My head was so empty that putting your ear to mine and listening to the blood rush, you could have heard the sea lap in my skull.

I went on dog walks and let the wind bounce my little fringe with every step, thinking things were good, and nowadays I could handle the mood swings, the skin problems, the doctor's fees, you know. Starting T would be easier now than ever. And I did always think of it as starting, somehow. It eased my guilt if I considered last time a trial run, something that was bound to end. This, though, this would be the real deal. But I couldn't keep my thoughts from meandering towards one funny question: *Why had this only occurred to me now, when I decided to grow my hair out?*

For the next while all my deliberations on hormone therapy were undercut by curious confusion, or confused curiosity. The dominant emotion varied by day. A mystery had fallen into my lap, and its difficulty frustrated me, but like with the best puzzles, I knew I would feel *so* good if I could solve it.

But in picking at that puzzle, I began to pull more questions out from inside the first, and as the whole thing unspooled, I found myself with increasingly unnerving threads of thought.

One in particular began ruining my peaceful dog walks:

Why does the image of myself on hormones feel alien?

And like grotesque ducklings behind it:

Why can I not describe this feeling?

Why do I picture hormones like a drop of blue paint in a yellow bucket, stirred, until there's no recovering the original colour?

Why do I want to preserve myself from this?

Why have I never met another trans person who started HRT but then changed their mind?

Am I allowed to change my mind?
Why did I start in the first place?

I concluded over and over that taking T could negate the feminine aspects of long hair, keep me androgynous at the least. I might get misgendered less. Maybe. It didn't make enough sense. It was not a good reason.

I said to my mother: 'I don't wanna get injections that'll change my body just to make other people more comfortable with me'.

She agreed, because it was a reasonable thing to say.

And the following week she came to a protest with me, a march to improve trans healthcare in Ireland, where trans people suffer every day without access to the hormone therapy I had just given up on. It did not feel so reasonable after all. I went home and walked the dog, puzzling.

I want to keep my body, and I want to keep it the way it is. A body I made for myself, the way I want it. A body that has merits and flaws galore and that I love, nonetheless.

I imagine changing my body for the comfort of strangers. Not for my kind mother, my loving friends, or the blissfully savvy arts block, but for people who will make big assumptions about me based on my appearance. People who must be, by this definition, strangers or cunts.

I imagine changing for them, and I'm ashamed to have considered it, and angry that I still consider it. My head is heavy to the point of collapse. It threatens to cave in my shoulders when I realise I have been distinguishing friends from strangers, when I should not change for anybody, no matter if I love them.

I know I'm not a woman, and my mother knows I'm not a woman, and my friends know I'm not a woman, but the strangers I greet in work say *excuse me thanks miss* and tell their children to *say thank you to the nice lady* because I smile when I take their ticket, and I am so nice to them, and they only mean to be nice back. And I just want, so badly, for their kindness to feel kind.

When I pause debating whether I should start T again, I start debating whether I ever should have started T in the first place.

There was a stretch in my late teens where I didn't know what to make of my body on T. My scope of transmasculine role models was narrow: I only knew of square, hirsute men or smooth, hairless androgynes. My body, girlish curves and prickly stubble, didn't look like any I'd seen before. It didn't look bad, but it didn't look like me anymore.

The stress of puberty hits differently when you know you did it to yourself.

That unexpected thought – *maybe I should start taking testosterone again* – had me wondering, to what end did I go through that period of anxiety? Because taking T was the 'done' thing, when you realise you aren't a girl? Because it was expected of me, as a step on every transition guide, as a criterion on every trans healthcare form? Because 'passing' has been touted all my life as the greatest achievement of the discreet transsexual?

I had collected frustrations over the years, but regret isn't part of the good trans narrative, so I swallowed them back. I couldn't open up about my reservations or I'd risk enabling anti-trans bigots and alienating peers who wanted to start HRT but couldn't. I stopped going to my trans youth group when some participants insisted that you had to hate your body to be trans, you had to want hormones and surgery with all your being, or it was probably just a phase. My trans friends celebrated their hormone anniversaries with gusto. I wanted to relate. I had to relate. I convinced myself that once I started T again I *would* relate.

Hormone therapy had come to mind like a reasonable counterpoint to growing my hair out, but it didn't tie back to any of *my* wants or desires. I couldn't retrace it, I couldn't find which part of my mind this idea had originated in. It might have felt so alien to me because it wasn't mine. It was the thought of another trans person which I had imposed on myself, one who fit a popular narrative of self-loathing and rebirth; it was the thought of the cis person who had invented that narrative.

In weeks spent deliberating *the thought*, I started a job involving bathroom checks. Within a month, I lost track of how many times a stranger walked in, saw me, and whipped around to check if he was indeed in the men's room. Some asked me where they were, others outright told me I was in the wrong bathroom. It was easy to point out my staff uniform, though I thought about telling them I was a man who just looked feminine, in the hopes of shifting the blame onto them.

But the thought of shutting away my transmasculinity moved me just as terribly as taking hormones I don't want, though this ache was in my chest rather than my thigh and my rough chin. Every stranger was a problem, and every solution had its own ache.

I've sometimes considered it a messy act of *giving* to go back on T. My mother told me before that I don't put my own needs first; I've ignored her, and realised after the fact that I gave far more than I got. It's not a romantic flaw. I am a limited supply of a person, so I dwindle. Some days I feel like I run out of me.

Taking T would give strangers an easier time understanding me. I'd give them a man just like them, that wouldn't make them double take at the bathroom sign, that they wouldn't overthink. I'd give them the gift of ignoring me. I'd fade away like every other stranger does.

Hormones wouldn't be the first thing I gave to strangers. I give them every minute of my life I spend picking clothes that are *me* but not so *me* as to invite misgendering. I give them the aches in my back from contorting into a chest binder. Every time I meet strangers (friends of friends) or strangers (off dating apps) or strangers (whose tickets I take and whose bathrooms I clean) I give them a censored version of myself with all the feminine edges sanded off, so everyone is happy, because they see the effort I put into beating my body, off T, into shape.

And I give and I give to strangers because I'm too nervous to do things for myself, and the strangers have validated self-flagellation every time. Taken my efforts to masculinise into consideration and rewarded me with a tepid 'sh – *he*' now and then, on the occasions they don't avoid pronouns entirely.

The strangers, who tell me it is difficult to understand a trans man who loves other men, it is too complicated to learn they/them, I am asking too much of them, have made any performance but the expected masculinity feel like an infliction on the world. And I am not a motivational story. Anything I give to others has to be the easiest, most ingestible version of itself: I must cook the sweetest food, I must write the loveliest words, I must be easy on the eyes, as in beautifully typical, as in not hard to process.

I've accepted that:

I was read as a woman when my hair was a medium tomboy length.

I was read as a woman when I shaved my head.

I was read as a woman when my hair grew out again and I kept it a cropped boy cut. Most bland styles I've sported didn't speak to my personality, but at least I looked like I was *trying* to be a man.

I've been so bland these last few years.

If it's all the same, I may as well grow my hair out. I say this to my co-workers when we arrive on the subject of haircuts, and I'm moaning that everyone gets praise for their new cuts, but nobody comments on the far more arduous process of growing your hair out. When they ask am I growing my hair out, I pat myself on the back for hooking them into the same old conversation, with experienced subtlety: yes, I am deviating from the narrative, so tell me I'm okay. I'm happier for it, tell me that's good for me.

Yeah, if it's all the same, and there's no controlling what strangers are gonna read on me, I may as well chase my bliss, I say.

A woman I met in work spotted that I was a new hire and asked my name. She's a regular. I said it was James and she said, 'It's nice to meet a young woman with a man's name'.

I laughed.

She smiled wistfully, 'There's a lot of men's names I'd like to have'.

'You can just do that', I encouraged. 'It's just a name. You can pick a new one if you fancy it'.

She laughed.

Neither of us understood how the other could possibly see the world, but we tried being kind, in our own ways. And I walked away aching from my head to my chest to my thighs.

I love Ally Beardsley, the trans comedian. And I love Ally's hair, dyed green on a dare, part-shaved for a challenge, shoulder length or flicking at the ears depending on the show I'm watching. As usual I don't know if I want to be them or be *with* them, but I know I want hair like theirs, and for the first time I feel an impulse to look more like a trans person than a cis one. A lot changed when I heard a trans person laugh on TV.

I still wonder what the alternative is to giving up on caring if cisgender people read me as a woman. I'm not strong or secure enough not to consider this a defeat. There's a lot I could do to minimise misgendering outside of hormones: I could change my wardrobe, get vocal training, try classic pre-T tricks of pubescent fandom forums like contouring your jawline. I could let my stubble grow out. But I would be doing it for the strangers.

And it is spring now, and I have not changed a lot since that club night in the Fringe. But my hair is a length where I can tie it up, and I have gleaned just enough confidence from the beautiful trans people around me to not do a thing for strangers or cunts.

What next?

- **The Small Trans Library** (*smalltranslibrary.org*) – The Small Trans Library is a small lending library of trans-authored books for trans people, with branches in Dublin and Glasgow.

an impersonal history of self-medication

by Kate Kiernan

This essay is dedicated to the memory of Larry Kramer, who passed away during its composition on 28/05/2020 and would have loathed the comparison.

AFTER READING ABOUT a woman who did it, I began to take the contraceptive pill in the summer of 2016. I was 24. Sometime before me in the late 1950s, this woman – as a girl of 12 – began taking contraceptive pills intended for her mother. Years later, she managed to convince doctors that she was intersex, and was able to access further healthcare on that basis.[1]

I was living in Chicago at the time and, with the support of one very dear friend there, had begun the process of coming out. I was not aware that I could have accessed hormone therapy properly in the US on an informed consent basis until I had returned to Ireland and re-entered my closet for a short time.

In Ireland, I continued to take the Pill with the help of my then partner – a transgender man. He left me the summer that followed, that of 2017, and decided he no longer felt comfortable helping me access the Pill. It was, in the end, a simple matter for me to go about accessing it on my own. I researched and selected a brand available in Ireland with a comparable oestrogen dose to that which most trans women start hormone therapy on. I got a prescription for it online and went about my business. At the same time, I contacted a GP, informed him that I intended to transition, and was placed on a ten-month waiting list for the Republic of Ireland's only gender clinic.

At the end of 2017, I joined a trans organisation focused on the arts, and began working with them on several projects. Through them, I met another trans man who helped me learn the basics of ordering oestrogen pills and blockers online (blockers like spironolactone are a cancer medication given to trans women for their testosterone-suppressant effects). By the end of 2018, the organisation was falling apart due to what I would call *interpersonal conflict* and what others would call *abuse*. It was a paradigmatic case of the failure in queer communities to meaningfully distinguish between conflict and abuse that Sarah Schulman had identified only two years prior in her dyke-titled book *Conflict Is Not Abuse*. Indeed, it was also paradigmatic of the legacy of the use of shame as a disciplinary tactic that Schulman had identified in her earlier, more impressive and less literally-titled book, *Ties That Bind: Familial Homophobia and Its Consequences*. I ended the year with my 'illegal' pills, exhausted from my stint as de facto mediator between various members of the organisation.

The collapse of that organisation continues to affect many of us who were involved with it. In all gay spaces these days, we encounter those queer cops who speak the online vernacular of queer politics so perfectly that they have completely forgotten what it is they are doing with their bodies. Physical existence is for them a function of the next boundary-smashing form of pop psychology or sexual practice that is out there, in Twitter's weeds. *Have I told you about how if you stick yourself with 1.5 inch drawing needles while reading* The Body Keeps the Score *you can make a lot of progress on your relationship with your parents and on your aesthetic at the same time?*

Well, now I'm just being a bitch.

In 2019, and after two years (not ten months) on a waiting list, I was able to see someone at the gender clinic. I told them I was self-medicating, and they gave me a prescription for what I was already taking, telling me it wasn't all that dangerous. I continued to self-medicate, but now determined for myself what form of oestrogen I would take (pill, patch, or injectable), and what dosage was right. That is the entire story, I'm afraid – four years of self-medication.

Would you like to know how many trans people are self-medicating in Ireland and the UK right now? Naturally, there are no studies, but here is an anecdote: the *majority* of all trans people I know self-medicate. How can this be?

Anyone with any connection to the trans community in Ireland or the UK knows that the state of trans healthcare in both countries is abysmal. It has become necessary and in some cases desirable for trans people to self-medicate. In the first case, because they cannot afford to wait the two, four, or even six years it can take to get a prescription.[2] In the second case, because they do not wish to be subject to the kinds of abuse and incompetence that frequently mark the gender clinic system; a system which is more invested in controlling access to hormone therapy as an exercise in power than it is in the wellbeing of trans people.

Less frequently discussed, and less well known, is the inequality that exists within trans communities: the trans people who cannot afford access (to hormone therapy or surgery), who do not know what their options are and have no community to turn to for advice, and the trans people who are betrayed by LGBT organisations which not only refuse to discuss the issue of self-medication but actively discourage organising around it. Another anecdote for you: in Ireland I attempted to establish a support group for those who self-medicate, the purpose of which was merely to discuss our experiences, and I have been refused help. Irish LGBT organisations have insisted that to accommodate such a group would be to put LGBT people in 'danger'. These organisations, including those led by trans people, have become spineless in their dependency on state funding and in their orientation towards inclusiveness programmes delivered to Deloitte and other companies within Ireland's financial services sector.

Any trans person in Ireland or the UK who wants hormones can have them *now*. All that stands in the way is the deliberate refusal of LGBT organisations to centralise information on how to access hormone therapy, make that information safe to access,[3] fundraise to make hormone therapy accessible to all,[4] and put direct pressure on doctors to work with the community in providing harm-reduction measures (like blood tests).[5] For a community with as much experience and activist nous as ours, this is not only achievable – *it is easy*.

Some will emphasise that self-medication is a private solution to a public problem, failing to understand that as much as the basis of gay power was coming out, the basis of trans power is access to this most basic element of trans healthcare. The medical-industrial complex cannot be effectively critiqued and transformed by those with no power over their own lives.

It tends to be lost on queers that when gays like Robert Duncan, Harvey Milk, or Larry Kramer were given the opportunity to gore heterosexuals on the long bull horns of gay passion, they chose instead to criticise their own communities.[6] It is easy to blame the heterosexuals – they are certainly as useless as blame – but as queers and gays, as the constituency of the limp wrist and the clenched fist, we must also look at ourselves. We are failing one another.

I would very much like to write an essay, someday, on my *personal* relationship with hormones. For now, my relationship with them is *impersonal*. That is how it must be until the day that every trans person can access them freely.

There are organisations that are working towards an informed consent model, based on what works in the US. I'm not sure this can work, because such a model crucially depends on leaving the medical resources in the hands of straight people, who are then to be convinced that it is their moral duty to give them to us. The approach that seems to me most likely to succeed is one in which LGBT organisations amplify the work of pre-existing self-medicating communities, with the ultimate goal of collective ownership of the means of safely producing and distributing hormones. This move towards collective ownership of LGBT resources by the community was originally proposed by Bruce Boone in 1979.[7] It is the right direction for our community to take: the resources that were originally created by the Gay Liberation movement, and which existed outside the control of state, have one by one been co-opted and toppled – the world of independent gay presses, bars, bookstores, and so on is inconceivable to the contemporary gay, who grows up comparatively rich in spirit of media but poor in flesh of love and fellowship.

Here is what I want to say to trans people in Ireland and the UK: Any trans person who wants hormones should be able to get them.

Here is what I want to say to LGBT organisations in Ireland and the UK: Communities of self-medicating trans people already exist. Your purpose is to respond to the lived reality of LGBT people, *not to shape or direct their lives*. Respond to what we are doing.

Today, I continue to self-medicate. I don't know how long this will continue. I do not wish to be at the mercy of straight doctors or, indeed, cis ones. I do not trust the people who tortured me for two years, refusing to see me and hand me a prescription they themselves knew to be harmless. I refuse to trust them because I watch them torturing my friends and loved ones in the same manner. I know that if I want access to some forms of surgery, I will have to go back to them and, undoubtedly, they will try to coerce me into entering into their care by threatening to cut off access to surgery.

Gays are a people of many closets. In 1969 the gays who were inspired by Stonewall said COME OUT,[8] in the late 1970s Harvey Milk said *come out, just come on out*, and we keep on coming out, but time is a Narnia of closeted intermissions and, now a movement in our fifties, we must be bold enough to imagine a new OUT to come out to. In working together on trans healthcare, gay people can heal divisions that have plagued us since 1969[9] while simultaneously *returning* to the politics of 1969.

What next?

- **Black on Both Sides: A Racial History of Trans Identity**
  by C Riley Snorton
- **Homosexual: Oppression and Liberation**
  by Dennis Altman

i'm wearing docs, michael

on thyroids, tallness, and teenage suffering

by Aifric Kyne

WHEN MY PARENTS were told about my condition, I was seven. My doctor told them that I would mostly be very tired for the next few years of my life and that I would have an occasional *goiter* on my neck which they needed to look out for if I was having trouble concentrating or seemed more detached than usual. The word *goiter* signified a swollen thyroid. It sounded ugly to me, even back then. I never liked it when they touched my neck and said *goiter* because at 10, 11, 15 I thought they were calling me ugly by association. It was barely noticeable to anyone who didn't know me but a swollen gland to someone like my mother meant looks of concern and constant monitoring.

Because the thyroid regulates puberty hormones, my doctor also told them that I would most likely hit puberty at a very young age. The hormonal aspect of something like an underactive thyroid isn't something a nine-year-old fully understands.

I got my first period in a church at my friend's First Holy Communion. I had no idea what was happening to me. I told my friend in the cubicle of a Chinese restaurant and we both stared at my underwear trying to figure out what it could be for what felt like a very long time. When I told my mother about it later that day, I couldn't understand why she was so upset. In retrospect, it was because I was only nine years old.

My doctor also told them it would affect my height. In my own research, an underactive thyroid normally results in stunted growth. The majority of the cases I read described young girls around the same age – eight or nine – who were too short for their age. In my case, and why to this day I'm still not clear, I was much taller than the average nine-year-old. In fact, I had almost reached my full adult height by the age of 13. This was the most enduring symptom of my condition, and as I grew older and began secondary school, my height became a major contributor to the issues I was having with my body image. While I was never in any physical pain, my wounds were internal and they manifested as an acute discomfort I felt about being in my body. My thyroid condition dictated the terms of my development, which was an extremely uncomfortable experience, permeating across all aspects of my life growing up.

i. *I just can't get that monster out of my head*[1]

When I was younger, I didn't know the meaning of body dysmorphia. I didn't understand that it was behind my refusal to look in mirrors or leave the house without layers of clothes and makeup on in my later teen years. I didn't know that not wanting to sit beside my peers in restaurants or bars, or even school lunch tables, was a disorder. Even now, associating myself with the word *disorder* feels melodramatic to me. It feels like a misguided diagnosis air-dropped on me by someone whose opinion I never asked for. If someone asked me what I thought about this, I would deny it.

I watched a number of girls in my year fade away in their own bodies for a long time with 'real eating disorders' and had no reference point to qualify what it actually meant to have a body disorder. I understand now that I was in a state of post-woundedness with my body. This idea of post-woundedness, from Leslie Jamison's *Empathy Exams*, defines the feeling of pushing a certain sadness or trauma aside. It is to brush feelings away in order to move from a wounded affect; it is to be 'in denial'. Most importantly, Jamison describes post-woundedness as not being a shift in feeling but 'a shift away' from the effect of feeling. It is to weave pain into your daily life, but not make it the focus of your daily life. It permeates through much more subtle channels: the opacity of a self-deprecating joke, a short story about a woman no longer fully in control of her feelings, feeling sad but not knowing the reason behind the sadness. In short, it's still there but *it is not a big deal*.

My body dysmorphia was 'not a big deal'. It still isn't — even though I had an hour-long therapy session where I discussed my complex feelings about bread last year; even though I still automatically remove myself from every photo I am tagged in for fear of anyone seeing me and realising what I actually look like. And yet, I am over it, much like, and even more so, my thyroid condition. My condition is secondary to the psychological wounds its symptoms left me with. The lack of thyroxine in my body wasn't my problem, the problem was how that lack of thyroxine manifested itself. Knowing the biological details of what an underactive thyroid entails doesn't mean much to me. I can't relate to them anymore, nor have I been able to for almost ten years. My height remains the only symptom of my alleged childhood condition. The chemical and hormonal activity of my body remains a mystery to me because when I ask my mother what was wrong with me, she always tells me the same thing: *You were tall, Aifric, you were a tall child.*

With age I have managed to align myself with my body, but it was harder to do so for the majority of my childhood and teenage years. My physical body and the essence of who I was were never in sync. I was often mistaken for a 16-year-old when I was 12. My own mother gave out to me for things she forgot 12-year-olds didn't understand because she forgot my age. My confusion at this often revealed on my face a vacancy which I imagine translated as hopelessness.

My friend Fatimah and I were at one point holding a secret club of womanhood behind the scenes of our primary school prefabs. We swapped pads like they were drugs and only spoke about it when we were alone, in the safety of her mother's flat down the road as she plied us with hummus and let us play *Mario Kart* after long days of feeling misaligned with our peers. The feeling of relief I felt when one by one each of my friends dropped the 'P-bomb' in the years following was almost comical. By 14, I was no longer alone and getting my period was merely a casual excuse for me to skip PE.

The plight I felt was for my physical appearance. I was disconnected from my reflection and on my worst days I avoided it at all costs to protect myself from what I thought would reveal to me the ugly reality of being a heaving shapeless blob. I imagined myself towering over everyone I walked past. Every act of clumsiness was magnified because to me, *tall* meant *clumsy*. Which meant that *I* was clumsy, which meant that I wasn't elegant, which in turn meant I wasn't beautiful. And while I didn't feel beautiful, I also felt like I was surrounded by beauty. 'Flinching' is a *cliché* used to symbolise not liking what you see in the mirror, but *clichés* are such for a reason; the girls' bathroom filled me with dread at school. There, I had no way of controlling what I saw in the mirror – there were days when I left my house without makeup filled with anxiety over the bareness of my face. It was on those days that I felt the most vulnerable, mirrors seemed to be everywhere – it felt inescapable, as I waited for my already naturally beautiful friends to make themselves more beautiful. I would stand there, all 5'10" of me exposed to the truth of my body. The acne that my doctor rated four on the scale of ten looked like a 20 on my skin. I mistook regular teenage spots for a haggard ruddy complexion and became fixated on trying to soften my face by scrubbing at it with harsh apricot exfoliators and acids because I thought I could burn the layer of badness off by over-cleansing. I gave up dairy at 16 because another doctor told me it would cure my mild acne. Certain foods became a source of anxiety for me and I began to trace any feelings of dissatisfaction I had with my appearance back to whether I had those foods that day. It was my way of coping with a body I felt I could not gain control over and I was compensating by being over-cautious about what I put into my body.

By the time I reached 18, I was a dairy-free hypochondriac with a number of complexes I could not begin to understand until much later into my twenties. It is only clear to me now, by writing this essay, just how lonely I was during that period of my life and how that feeling of not being at one with my body permeated through many aspects of my everyday actions and decisions, consciously or otherwise.

ii. *Skeleton you are my friend*

In 'Mariella', Kate Nash sings about going mute to find a richer connection to the outside world. At first, it seems as though Nash is lamenting her inability to control her impulsive nature. However, the song develops into a story about a young girl who has glued her lips together. The story is told in the voice of her mother who is in despair at the rejection she feels from her little girl. Mariella throws all her colourful clothes away and replaces them with black ones instead. She finds strength in her self-containment and 'skips down the road' at the empowerment she feels in 'knowing all the secrets in her world'. She also gains a new-found insight into the world which Nash implies she wouldn't have if she had stayed the same as the other girls her age.

For years after I heard this song, I felt an affinity with Mariella. I could empathise with her motives, though there are no motives mentioned in the song. I read it as an allegorical tale about protection through self-containment. I took this and used it for my own protection: I used to write a short story series about a similar character called Annabelle, who was inspired by Mariella. She was a young, delicately built girl who was a loner with only a cat for a friend and wore rubber boots. She was mute, which became her primary characteristic throughout. I eliminated parents from her story like in a Bildungsroman to give her the freedom of an orphan without her actually being one. Annabelle's muteness was a symptom of a childhood trauma she was not yet mature enough to articulate. I passed off her refusal to speak as the foible of a child that lived in her own little bubble, without realising that this was my way of communicating the pain I was in in my own body. Annabelle was a post-wound study of the state of self-containment to which I often found myself adapting in order to survive my teenage years.

Being an only child, I was well used to self-containment. I enjoyed it as a default existence. Annabelle was not, however, a melancholic character, nor is Mariella. They both had the chipper accessibility of a children's book but there was a hidden sadness in both girls. When I think about how I presented Annabelle and how Kate Nash presents Mariella, one obvious feature of both of them is that they are pre-pubescent. Nash longs for Mariella's pre-hormonal eloquence and ability to stay out of trouble, while I longed for not only that but also a way I could disconnect from my own body. I wanted some part of me to still remain a child who actually looked like a child. I wanted to reject my curves because when they came, I wasn't ready for them. I was rejecting myself through my own creative process – rejecting my body; rejecting my voice; rejecting my growth. Annabelle's appearance was the opposite of mine. She was short and blonde with the build of a child. She was *small*. She had what I craved for myself.

Last year I went through an old laptop of mine and found photos from when I was 18, when my dysmorphia was at its worst. When I found the file, I was worried about looking through it and how I'd react to seeing myself at the highest point of my unhappiness. I was expecting to find myself as I remembered – 18, spotty, overweight, awkward, and lumbering. To my surprise, I found images of a girl who looked completely normal to the outside world. She was glowing from all the running she had taken up and her hair was the longest it had ever been. Looking at the girl in the photos and remembering how unhappy she was further proved to me how out of sync I was with my body. The lack of empathy I had for myself was the true root of my issues as a teenager, and had I been a little easier on myself, my height and my hormones probably wouldn't have been such an issue for me.

I haven't needed to go to the doctor for my thyroid for almost ten years. My *goiter* is no longer there which means no more *ugliness* on my body. The only evidence left from my condition is the crackling of my joints that happens when I am sitting on an overly cramped bus or train carriage. I tell people as a joke when referring to my height that I am *mostly all leg* and when I subject my body to sitting in a space for which I am physically too big, it protests by cramping up and begs me to stretch it out. When I used to try to make myself smaller by slouching over, I wasn't listening to my body. I was folding it into a shape against its will and forcing it to be something it wasn't. Now, in my late twenties, it is the one who speaks first.

What next?

- **YoungMinds** *(youngminds.org.uk)* – YoungMinds are a charity leading the fight for a future where all young minds are supported and empowered, whatever the challenges.

spinning through fog

(high salt content)

by Ali Maloney

As I cook, the sizzle of chillies searing in the wok wafting over me, my head droops and my will slumps. The only thing that keeps me going is knowing that if I collapse, hot oil would splash over me; a fire would likely start, something in my mind rushes to remind me. Is this how I'd want my corpse to be found?

It is an inkling that is never far from thought. I go through most days almost giddy from light-headedness. Like being lulled by the motion of a long bus journey, the sensation of trying to defy falling asleep is a constant. Only, I worry, it is not sleep that would get me if I just *stopped*.

Over a period of several days in 2014, on life support in the intensive care unit of St John's Hospital, I was diagnosed with a rare, incurable, life-threatening disease that requires life-long steroid dependency. If I don't take enough, the world becomes a sluggish and confusing murk through which I struggle to wade; if I take too much, I am almost certain to develop osteoporosis. However, endocrinologists try to keep my dosage at the lower end of that spectrum. My life has transformed, different in almost every regard, since diagnosis – and almost entirely for the better.

I was working in a lowly admin job with a baby at home. The onset of symptoms was so gradual that they had each been discounted or explained away. When I'd stand up after, say, bending down to tie my shoelaces, I'd be so dizzy that I'd fall over. I honestly just thought that's what life was like when you were in your 30s. I vomited several times a week and, of course, just thought I was struggling to get over some mysterious bout of food poisoning.

Up until then, I was healthy and rarely ill. In retrospect, I should have known something was wrong but, at the time, it seemed obvious: it was the result of getting older and the exhaustion and pressures of a small child. I lost an incredible amount of weight and people kept remarking how tanned I was so I thought '*I must be doing something right*'.

Throughout all this, I was eating an incredible amount of salt. Five or six single serve sachets of it would be sprinkled into a bag of crisps and it still wasn't enough. The craving was overwhelming. Of course, every time someone saw me eating salt like this they'd chastise me or remind me how unhealthy it was. I developed a secret habit; surreptitiously pouring it on food or keeping salt mixed in with herbs to hand.

Slowly, as it started to dawn on me that *something* wasn't right, I just assumed I had developed a deeply unhealthy addiction to salt. Much later, when I eventually returned to work, I found little stashes of salt packets hidden everywhere. While I was being wheeled into the Intensive Care Unit, they said that my salt levels were so low that I was literally hours away from death. I wanted to laugh at that, to tell them that was impossible; that I had pretty much been going through a whole salt shaker a day. But I was too weak to do anything at that point.

In the lead up to this, I had been off sick from work several times with those stomach bugs and dizziness; those warning signs I shouldn't have ignored. My manager said if I was off one more time, I'd be on a formal review. Being such a conscientious person, I really didn't want that. So when I eventually collapsed and could not get up again, pain searing through my muscles, I did not want to phone NHS 24. I wanted to sleep it off and go to work the next day. My partner at the time, the mother of my children, insisted. I was later told that if I had gone into work like I wanted to, I would have dropped dead.

She was not the last person to save my life that day.

Hurried into an ambulance, I was taken into A&E where I lay in the corridor amongst all the Saturday night drunks. During my triage, they could find no cause for alarm and were arranging the paperwork to send me home, despite my protestations of being unable to stand. I saw someone running through the ward towards us, frantically waving for the attention of the nurse standing over me. My blood charts had found their way to a specialist consultant somewhere in the hospital who had noticed some frightening anomaly. He stopped my discharge and had me transferred to the Intensive Care Unit.

I was giddy and delirious as a catheter was slid into me. A nurse held my head down with all her weight lest I move while the tubes for dialysis were slid down a hole in my neck. I was almost completely out when the oxygen mask was slipped over me.

It took them a couple days to figure out what was wrong.

It would be remiss of me not to mention that this was over Easter: when I was as close to death as I care to be, for three days, before coming back. Feel free to draw your own conclusions from that.

Autoimmune Addison's Disease is a rare endocrine condition in which the adrenal glands cease to function. The adrenal glands produce and regulate a whole suite of hormones which keep the body functioning correctly. My body no longer has the ability to do that. Why? During some bout of illness, a year or two prior to my collapse, my immune system went a bit trigger-happy on an indiscriminate rampage and killed off my adrenal glands while attacking whatever virus was in my body at the time. Apparently, it is as simple as that.

John F Kennedy had Addison's Disease. It was responsible for that tanned look he always had, as well as the several times he collapsed. I am yet to establish whether or not I too shall have an affair with Marilyn Monroe and be assassinated. I have heard rumours that Florence Nightingale and Osama Bin Laden were likely to have it – which is some very mixed company to keep. I am almost certain the sickly trailer park child in the film *Independence Day* had it.

I take steroids regularly to replace those my body no longer produces naturally. My ability to regulate blood sugar and pressure, electrolyte and fluid balance, metabolism, and libido is entirely artificial. These are things you probably do not give a second thought to – but trust me, you miss them when they are gone.

If I miss a dose, I become completely unable to function. A dense, black fog rolls over my mind and muscles, bringing confusion and the sensation of trying to move through tar. If I am ill, I need to take extra to bolster a compromised immune system. I wear a medical alert bracelet as, if I were in an accident, my body would not have the normal spike of adrenaline that a shock response provides, so I would need an immediate injection to keep me alive (my endocrinologist is not happy with me having an injection kit, so let's just hope any attending ambulance has one). Too high a dose brings the risk of osteoporosis for which I regularly have bone scans.

With the right balance, there is no reason why someone with Addison's can't live a long, healthy, productive life. But balance is a tricky thing. Our bodies' needs are constantly changing. A course of tablets needs to be largely rhythmic and, therefore, somewhat inflexible. My vitality revolves around these replacement hormones – as opposed to the other way around, a functioning hormone regulation which adapts to the body's needs and rises up to support your life. This can be debilitating.

Of course, everyone diagnosed with Addison's Disease experiences and lives with it differently. Perhaps one day, my dosage or medication will change and all of this will seem a distant memory, either for the better or the worse.

If I don't take my medication, I would die within a day or two without medical intervention. Death is never an abstract concept for me and the daily use of steroids ensures that it is never far from my mind. Survival requires my constant, active participation. It is just as well that I am of such a cheery and optimistic disposition.

I am entirely reliant on pharmaceutical companies' manufacturing and distribution chains. I have read that before the necessary steroid replacement was developed, some patients could be kept alive by being fed minced pig adrenal glands but, if it all goes *Walking Dead/Mad Max* out there, I honestly wouldn't know what to do.

As well as the risk of osteoporosis and muscle wasting, there are more immediate symptoms and side effects with which I contend daily.

I am constantly thirsty. I can feel utterly dehydrated but, when I down a pint of water, I pee it out almost instantly, not even vaguely sated. This is the kind of curse that belongs in a mythology book. Salt sorts me right out though, as it helps retain water; a salty snack with a drink is a necessity. It is good then that I have a very savoury tooth.

Fatigue weighs me down. My days are clouded with exhaustion. I frequently wish, loudly, to anyone who'll listen, that after-lunch siestas were a societal norm in the workplace, and I am not joking. My blood pressure is consistently low, which means whenever I stand up too quickly, light-headedness overwhelms me. Low blood pressure has ramifications across my life.

One of the listed side effects (uncommon, affects about 5 in every 100 people) is that of 'an all-consuming sense of impending doom' which I am almost sure I have not experienced, which is quite remarkable given everything that is happening in the world right now.

The steroid dosage I am taking has given me gout, flare-ups of which are blindingly painful and are aggravated by the salty foods I need to stay hydrated. The skin pigmentation that is a major symptom of Addison's Disease is starting to escalate from a handsome, healthy-looking tan into rapidly appearing blotches of freckles over my face. When I need to up my dosage as a replacement for an immune system – if, for example, I have a cold – my face bloats and swells in what is commonly referred to as 'moon face'. These may be small, superficial things, but they can weigh on the self-conscious.

I definitely present as a strong, confident guy full of enthusiasm and energy. I bound between several creative projects, a demanding full-time job, my two beloved children and the eight-hour round trip I regularly take to see them.

Thirsty, tired, and dizzy, I go through my days. But the

urge to just lie down and do *nothing* is tempered by the urges to be creative and productive and fruitful and to be human. I am not giving up.

At the beginning of the Jim Jarmusch film *Ghost Dog: Way of the Samurai*, Forest Whitaker muses that the samurai should meditate on death every day – to imagine all the ways, both vicious and ridiculous, that he could be killed – in order to find a peaceful path through life. This sentiment resonates with me a lot. Having been so close to death myself and the regular reminders of my own mortality has changed my outlook tremendously. I have gone after opportunities that I previously would have shied away from. I have put myself forward for things that, before, would have had me cowering. Since diagnosis, I have found and prospered in a new career, my artistic projects have been grander and more successful; I have learned to drive, bought a house, learned new skills, got fit; made so much more with my time. Because what have I got to lose? I am now more confident, more settled in my skin, more certain of my abilities; stronger, and yet…

My energy requires constant vigilance. Stress or worry absolutely wipe me out. If I do not meticulously pace myself, I can end up spending days in bed. As a consequence, I am very mindful on where my energy and focus are spent. This mindfulness can mean having to cancel things last minute or trying to stick to a schedule I know will allow me to rest during days. Both of these things can make me seem antisocial or reclusive, I know. It's the price I pay for doing stuff; for keeping busy – the alternative is doing *nothing*.

What next?

- **Addison's Disease Self-Help Group**
  (*addisonsdisease.org.uk*) – Addison's Disease Self-Help
  Group supports people affected by Addison's Disease,
  a rare endocrine disorder in which the adrenal glands do
  not produce enough steroid hormones.

everything and nothing

on pregnancy and depression

by Fiadh Melina

IT WAS 3AM,

Or maybe it was 4 or 5. Time tends to blur when you want it to stop. And I really did want it to stop.

There was a brand new, tiny human in a glass cot beside my bed. There was an irregular rhythm of sleep, nurse, nappies (for both of us), nurse, sleep, cry (for both of us), sleep. Until I gave up and had to ask for them to take her away. They had to care for my little one, not because of the agony in my overturned gut post-caesarean, not because I wished her any ill-will (that's what they liked to assume was wrong with me), but because I wasn't sure how I was going to take another breath.

'It's fine, it's just the hormones', said the woman in pale blue scrubs when I told her my head wasn't ok. That I needed someone to talk to because my head wasn't good to me.

'It happens to everyone'. I don't remember her name. There were so many lovely midwives that helped me in those days and nights, but I'm shaking as I write this, remembering how this one woman looked at me and didn't believe that I needed help. Beyond the protocol of postpartum hormone surges.

She was meant to be the gatekeeper to this new world I'd entered;

Motherhood.

But I was left flatlining.

As it turns out, there is no gatekeeper or guide when it comes to our brains, because we're all so ridiculously individual. But it's hard to see the beauty of individuality when you're sitting in the midst of snotty tissues and a face stiff from tears.

Though I like to say I'm a writer, I find the act of putting words to this particular story rather difficult. Well...almost impossible, really. I'm spinning through sparse, mostly barren memories – a great side effect of trauma – and converging worlds of stigma and taboo. Depression and unplanned pregnancy during the height of a vicious abortion rights campaign was not a recipe for sanity.

But I found myself an outlet.

One strange artefact that emerged during that year was poetry, so I'm going to use a few of those pieces as benchmarks for this essay. If you're sighing at this point thinking 'oh not another one of those overdone Instagram poems', well, same. Maybe they won't make it past the first draft, but for now they'll act as a looking glass into the memories my mind still hides in fog.

it's like homesickness
for my old life
but i can never
go back because the
house burnt down.

When I look at my daughter today, whether her face is spread into a pearly, toothy grin, scrunched in a mid-tantrum scowl, or covered in buttery rice cake; I love her. I never understood quite how deep and vast that emotion could go. I had never been *in* love, so it was all an abstract idea that someday might strike – if it existed at all. When I look at her now, my heart squeezes and flutters because I can't quite believe how anything so perfect – even covered in buttery rice cake – could exist. She's everything. 'Everything' is the best definition I can give to love, because even when you're empty, it fills up all the cracks and glues you back together just to allow you to stand in one piece for another day.

Two years ago, I wouldn't have believed there was ever a thing that could glue me to the world. I was floating someplace liminal; not quite here, not quite gone.

This is when I first came up against 'it's just the hormones'. Repeatedly. From friends and acquaintances, doctors and psychiatrists. Those who probably thought they were normalising my experience, turning it into something tangible, but they only managed to alienate me further. It completely nullified anything I did feel, which was a terrifying, all-consuming loneliness. As a hardcore introvert by nature, being alone has never equated to loneliness, and in the same way I learnt what love is, I became acquainted with what it truly felt to be lonely.

I couldn't relate to happy, pregnant people, couldn't relate to my friends who didn't understand how it felt to have something growing inside them, couldn't relate to the numerous people who said, 'it's only nine months, it'll fly by'. 90% of the latter group have never had severe depression or been pregnant. Time turned to mud. Happiness turned stale. Friends became foreign.

I felt sick; homesick for a life I hadn't gotten the chance to say goodbye to. You know the grating feeling you get in your gut when you're about to do something you really wished you hadn't signed up for? Imagine that and then add a tornado of homesickness. Let's call it dread on steroids.

I was burning yesterday
when you told me swimming
was easy
and all I had to do
was paddle

I kept coming against a dull thud of 'but you're so lucky you can have a baby! Think of all those who can't', which is a scary echo of the stigmatic 'but people have it so much worse than you' that gets tossed at someone who's depressed, or anxious, or suicidal. It creates shame towards feeling anything at all and snubs validity of those feelings. You're then expected to explain yourself, or to take the more socially acceptable road and apologise. 'You're right, sorry. Yes, yes, of course. I'm very grateful. How could I be so selfish?'

I didn't apologise most of the time. I don't tend to apologise for existing in my truth, so I usually sat in silence because if I spoke, I might have thrown up. There were lots of silent tears; on buses, in small counselling rooms, in the car. Always, I'd second guess their origin. *My feelings or my hormones?* Because that's what I'd been told to do. Over and over. What I *knew* was overwritten by repetition of those whose lives were made easier by relegating my responses to a compartmentalised side effect, rather than my individual experience.

And then I was slapped in the face. Several times. Both by people I loved and by strangers, whose job description essentially said 'I'm here to help' (the small font always seemed to say 'one second while I put you in a stereotype box and recite answers rather than listen to your individuality'). Professionals can blame hormones as the causes for hurt because it's easier than facing the fact we are functioning individuals (even if we're going through a rather terrible phase of dysfunction).

'Alien in your belly'

'Hormonal'

'So weird'

'Hormones'

There was a cavity in my chest. Squeezing down on my heart and lungs, growing every time another person told me I couldn't be sad. They could joke, it wasn't a part of them. A friend, I was, yes. A best friend, absolutely. But no matter how present they were, my pregnancy was still an abnormality too far off to grasp, so jokes were easier. But jokes meant people didn't believe my brain was a mess when I told them.

It wasn't a friend who told me an alien was in my stomach. Thankfully, because that would have been much worse. One of the first psychiatrists I went to said it. She was trying banter with a 23-year-old girl who felt more alien than ET. Whose belly had started to flutter, not with nerves, but kicks. She prescribed my meds and I could never look her in the eye again. I requested a different psychiatrist for future sessions, but I was forced to sit with her again at the very end when I signed off 'suicide watch' and was back off to college. I still feel sick when I think about her. I can say for sure she affected me far more negatively than any hormone ever has.

She looked to her moon and shed silent tears as despair
clutched her lungs and whispered 'you will never reach
her'

I think contradictions are a huge part of that year.

Case 1: I don't like counselling, I don't find it helpful for my own weird, floaty brain experience, but I went to several counsellors over two years.

Case 2: I don't like taking brain meds, but I still am.

Case 3: Everything felt out of my control. No matter how much I resisted living each day, the night would inevitably come, and then the next morning, and again and again the next day came, until it all flatlined. Something went off with the bile in my pancreas and everything stopped. I thought I'd lose her because I hadn't been eating, because of so many terrible thoughts I'd had. As much as I didn't want any of it happening, I couldn't imagine anything worse than having harmed her. She was already everything.

I told one Pieta counsellor that I was 'floating' because 'existing' felt too steady, too tangible a verb. I still float, a lot. I did a lot before I was pregnant too. Which is why I knew what my brain was doing to me. I've had plenty of years to become acquainted with how my floaty brain functions, and sometimes explaining it doesn't go very well, but she was nice about it. Then she made me pick stones from a glass bowl for each member of my family. She lost me there, to be honest.

Picture a little person in a chunky space suit, dangling off a wire on the International Space Station. That's the cinematic, pretty version of what floating looks like. But there's no air; and that was accompanied by deep, intensely negative emotions. 'Floating' and 'emotions' sound incompatible, and they are. They leave you hanging.

I have this weird thing. Last year, a college counsellor called me arrogant because I was trying to explain it to him. I tend to have a very blank mind. It's hard to explain because it kind of goes against all logic, but I recently found a random blog post that explained *there are others who don't think too*, so it must legit be a thing.

The college counsellor labelled me as 'arrogant'. Not in his notebook, which is what I'd have glanced at if I was in a movie and he was scribbling intellectual observations. No, it was spoken to my face. He told me I didn't want help, that I didn't try enough. I had never realised there were benchmarks for trying when it came to saving your own life. Making the appointments, coming in the door and sitting on the chair didn't seem to count even though to me, they might as well have been a journey to the moon and back. I understood he needed a back-and-forth, but when I explained I didn't have thoughts in my head which make it hard to speak sometimes, he said 'I don't believe you'. He stood by the opinion that, rather than telling him the truth, I was being lazy and fabricating this existence of 'no thoughts'. It triggered the misbelief and constant friction I had been met with during pregnancy and in the first months after birth, when 'my hormones were wild'.

Another gatekeeper was telling me that my truth wasn't true. What are you meant to do with that?

I wish I had an answer. My head still hurts.

Tears
It was reality.
The fantasy crashed
And she could no longer pretend to be
Dreaming

I still struggle with all of this.

Bodily autonomy is something I never understood until I was pregnant. I became as actively involved in the Repeal the 8th campaign as I could between tides of debilitating depression, fatigue, and migraines. For anyone not aware of what Repeal the 8th was, it was the abortion rights campaign which repealed the anti-abortion laws in Ireland, and conveniently raged alongside the first half of my pregnancy. I had released a little spoken word Repeal poem a few years before but becoming pregnant and being faced with a choice that didn't actually exist became the catalyst for my participation, and my mind's suffering. It wasn't hormones driving my mind to abyss. It was photoshopped pictures of foetuses sprawled on banners across College Green or at the entrance of my own college, or on O'Connell Street, while a real one grew inside me. It was millions of people thinking they could decide what my body was made for. Production. Nothing else. That sentiment runs sinister and deep. It doesn't stop at the abortion laws we successfully repealed. The way society has constructed women in relation to men, and in relation to their own children, means that they come second. We come second. While I will always put Selene before me out of pure instinct, this is different to the decisions of people who simply believe it's their right to decide for you. It feels like you're in a terrible dream where you're in a burning house and someone's shrieking at you to deal with it, drowning out your own thoughts and feelings in the process. Only it's real, and the people are your neighbours who you've never spoken to before, and they want you to stay in the burning house if you choose autonomy.

The blank mind thing actually really helps with writing fiction – things just flow subconsciously, it's all sunshine and daisies. But it's probably exactly why writing this piece is so hard. Not only am I setting my mind to a function it doesn't naturally do, I'm also fighting against side effects of its trauma. I have a bad memory in general but blank spots (or chasms) are especially potent during my 'floating' times. I guess my mind runs from it because who would want to relive it? Definitely not me. I suppose I've just made us all relive it a little bit now; another contradiction.

Moon scene; everything.

I named my daughter Selene Radha, a name I'd decided upon when I was about 16 and joking with my friends about baby names (hah). Selene is the Titan goddess of the moon in Greek mythology, and Radha comes from the Irish word for 'radharc', meaning 'scene' or 'vision'. *Moon scene.* And she really is. Just a glittering ball of smiles and joy. I feel like there's a lot of power in people's names, and even through pregnancy, when my head was trying to destroy me from the inside out, when I couldn't eat, sleep or speak; I was able to find a little bit of solace in watching the peaceful moon. Thankfully we had clear skies that summer.

To watch Selene grow into that name day-by-day is, well, everything.

What next?

- **PANDAS Foundation** *(pandasfoundation.org.uk)* – PANDAS is here to help support and advise any parent and their networks who need support with perinatal mental illness.

ten years in the making

conversations with partners about
polycystic ovary syndrome

by Sonali Misra

WE NEED TO talk.

Let me preface this by saying: this is not a huge deal. I only
want to tell you a story. A story of me one day waking up and
realising that the part of my body I'd cursed ever since the
first red spot bloodied my clothes – the one that women were
biblically punished with – had finally heeded my words and
fucked off, only to leave me alone like a repentant lover. But
this story is not just my own. It is the story of countless others
scattered across the globe.

I had never heard of 'polycystic ovarian disease', which
is what it was called before it became a syndrome sometime
in the past ten years. What a shocker, right, considering the
thorough sex education that we receive in schools, whether
here in the UK or back in my home country, India? I found

out about the condition when a follicle in my ovary swelled up and burst, leading up to hours of the most excruciating pain I've ever experienced – and I say this as someone who's fractured a foot. There was a lot of doubling over, clutching my abdomen and screaming in pain; a lot of wondering what horrible thing I'd eaten that poisoned my body. Mum thrust home remedy after home remedy into my hands – fennel seeds, cloves, *isabgol* – when none of the painkillers we had on hand worked. We finally went to hospital, where an ultrasound scan revealed numerous tiny harmless-looking squiggles in my ovaries.

This was in January 2010 in Gurgaon, India. I remember the time because this incident occurred amidst my 'preboards' – the practice examinations before the actual twelfth-grade board examinations that Indian children believe will determine the rest of their lives. The searing abdominal pain isn't a usual symptom of PCOS, or so I was told, and it was brushed aside as a one-off incident. It wasn't. It happened again in my mid-twenties, and my boss rolled her eyes at it. I wasn't outright told that I had to continue working, but I clearly had no choice. Heavy pain medication was my only reprieve, apart from resting my head on my desk and groaning in between tasks. It didn't end up mattering that my manager was a woman. Perhaps because PCOS is so common now, I shouldn't have expected any preferential treatment? Or maybe because there's no information online about the links between PCOS and pain, she thought I was exaggerating, making excuses to shirk off work?

I know, I know it's annoying when I tell stories out of order. Okay, back to 2010. Doctor appointments followed, and since my periods weren't too infrequent, I wasn't put on any medication, just told to lose weight by fixing my diet and exercising. Having been overweight since I hit my teens, I was used to hearing this at every visit to the doctor. To an 18-year-old Sonali, none of it sounded too bad, honestly. In fact, it explained away the weight gain, 'tomboy' tendencies and excess body hair – did you know I prepare for our dates with an elaborate routine involving bleaching, threading, waxing, shaving? So, I thought: maybe I'm not a freak after all and this illness is to blame for everything. Pregnancy and the issues PCOS could cause for it, as well as the possibility of developing Type 2 diabetes, seemed so far away. And, *surely*, I would implement all the recommended lifestyle changes by then?

You laugh because you've beaten me to the punchline: obviously, as you can see, I did not.

I also wondered: so what if the gaps between each period increased? Cumulatively, I would then have to deal with fewer cramps, mood swings and times I'd have to wash stains off my clothes every year, and that just sounded like a relief. Plus, I had been facing exam-related anxiety, and this gave me a reason not to study or hold myself up to my usual high standards. I even left the three-hour physics exam after just one – unheard of, really – and crashed into my strict teacher in the corridor, who only let me go, red-faced under his striking moustache, once I used the word 'ovaries' in my explanation while pointing at my abdomen.

My parents were taking it hard, though. My teddy-bear-of-a-mother's life revolves around my brother and me, and she takes our health concerns seriously. I now only tell her that I'm ill when it's serious as, ironically enough, she worries herself sick over it. However, my always-calm-in-the-face-of-emergencies father fretted too. He even bought a lengthy e-book with advice from some fancy American doctor about treating PCOS, since it's incurable. I never got around to reading it. Exasperated, Dad finally read it himself and gave me the highlights. Ten years later, the only thing I remember from it is that we're supposed to drink cranberry juice; a *lot* of it.

I know we've only been dating for a few weeks, and I'm not sure if there's a science to it or whether some instinct helps me pick the right moment to have this conversation. There probably isn't even a *right* time. But we're at that age now when we hope certain relationships will last long-term and we make plans for the future. And we've been getting close…so, you deserve to know.

Before I move on, let me clarify: my parents' primary concern is that PCOS may lead to other health complications, like diabetes, high cholesterol and even cancer. Growing up, I never discussed the subject of romantic relationships with them, but I wonder what crossed their minds when they learnt that I may have trouble conceiving – did they worry about my future or my 'marriageability', an aspect that is considered an essential part of a woman's identity, no matter what background she hails from? I would categorise my parents as progressive, even if our political views don't always match: once Mum jokingly said that they had enough savings to either throw me a lavish wedding, which is the norm in the Punjabi and North-Indian Hindu community, or pay for my master's degree tuition fee in Scotland. Dad and I said 'studies' in unison. My education, my career, my achievements were never treated as 'less than' because I was the daughter or the younger child. In fact, I couldn't have asked for more supportive parents. But I do believe that my life has been less contentious because my desires align with what society deems appropriate for a woman: get married to someone of the opposite sex and have children.

Don't freak out. Yes, I've dropped the dreaded M- and C-words, but I don't mean it's what I've planned specifically for you and me. Of course it's too soon – I don't even know your favourite ice cream flavour, whether you sleep in bed with your socks on, or what setting you put your thermostat at, let alone when you want kids or if you even want them.

Salted caramel? Okay, more chocolate in the world for me then.

You know, Teenage Sonali despised kids, though they tended to love her somehow. Then I hit my twenties, and it's as if something other than a fluid-filled sac in my ovaries exploded every time I saw a baby. Perhaps it was due to the birth of my cousin's daughters, which led to sustained contact with babies and seeing them grow up to be more than just screeching monsters who destroy everything they touch. But in order to have kids, I'd have to get married first (if I'm still following the ways of my community), and I haven't always had the best luck with relationships. A lot of it is owing to my own self-esteem issues regarding my weight, but even when I feel that I've defeated those demons, it is plainly obvious that I don't fit into society's idea of what a woman's body should look like; I'm used to being the less-popular romantic choice for men. Of course, you might say I could always opt for arranged marriage since I'm Indian. I don't believe it is for me though – marriage is a commitment I would make to someone I loved and wished to spend the rest of my life with, not an item to tick off my checklist – but I know it's not even an option that I could really consider. With the way arranged marriages have been commercialised through matrimonial websites and agencies requiring a detailed 'CV' that even lists women's heights and weights, I'm sure that my profile would get left swipes, or whatever the marital equivalent to it is. Pressing an 'X', instead of the 'O' representing the engagement ring?

My parents have known about my views regarding arranged marriage for years, but ever since I crossed the age at which my mother got married, ten days short of 27 – quite late for her time – they've been asking me if they should 'start looking for someone'. When I first moved to Scotland for my studies, Mum visited me and we got the opportunity to travel and live together for two whole months, just us, without the men in my family for once. Renting a flat on the Isle of Bute, she and I learnt to recognise and befriend each other as adults, and I began opening up to her about relationships. And now she grills me about every man I date to ensure that I choose someone who could potentially be my long-term partner, so that I can catch up to my peers and finally shoot out babies.

But what if I can't even have kids?

While medication and technology exist to aid the process of conception for those inflicted with PCOS, they don't always work. Over the years, I've had to warm myself up to the idea of adoption. A secret smile tethered to my heart always appears whenever someone says that I'm a 'carbon copy' of my mother (though heavier than she was at my age, as some of my extended family might add). I like looking at my parents and tracing what exact mixture of their features gave birth to my face. I have my father's nose and long arms and the bunion that runs in his line; my mother's round face and curls and weak eyes. My adoptive child wouldn't carry forth any of these. But then I remember that I also have my father's wit and passion for storytelling and desire to help others; my mother's goofiness, extroverted nature and fair-dealing hand – and I could always pass on these qualities to my child, biological or not.

As rational as this reasoning now sounds to me, it has been ten years in the making. It may be odd to commemorate the tenth anniversary of a medical diagnosis, but the fears and anxieties related to it have been my constant companions this past decade: from the comfort of being a child at school, to becoming an adult who did her taxes but still lived in the protected palm of her home, then moving to another corner of the world where every face she met was new. One such face has been yours. And with you, like my past relationships, I've been forced to add an extra step in the dating timeline, a disclaimer of sorts, due to the PCOS. It usually sits somewhere between the waning of the honeymoon period and the start of heated arguments. Sometimes I try to slip it in casually in the first few days. The whole thing is almost funny and ridiculous though. You know how if you're remorseful about doing something terrible in the past – cheating, lying, breaking your partner's trust – and wish to reveal all, every facet, of yourself to someone who could be *It?* I instead have to confess that I have PCOS and may not be able to bear children – and hope for the best. Each time, I've been forced to run through an entire explanation to contextualise this condition and make them understand what it is and how it's affected me. It becomes less emotionally draining with every retelling; more like a fact of my life. Which it is, and I know it to be a fact for so many out there born with ovaries.

Maybe I should've just made my life simpler by writing down the narrative on paper, so that I could shove it under my partner's nose and wait for their reaction.

But anyway. What do *you* think?

What next?

- **Vatsalya Foundation** (*sakhi-vatsalya.org*) –
  Vatsalya Foundation focuses on menstrual hygiene of underprivileged girls. They conduct training camps, and provide educational kits to explain menstruation, and offer support and guidance to sufferers and their families.

clot

by Rachel E Moss

ON A DREARY June day in 2017, I sat in a reclining chair while a young woman with a shock of cobalt hair injected radioactive tracer into my arm. I said I felt like Spiderman and she laughed, confiding that you don't *have* to be a nerd to work in Nuclear Medicine, but it helps. A little while after that, I lay very still inside a machine, looking up at a ceiling decorated with twinkling lights, breathing in krypton gas and waiting for my superpowers to kick in.

What I got instead was a pulmonary embolism – a blood clot in my lung. Or in my case, three clots, tiny specks of darkness floating in a space where there should be nothing. They were classed as small, only pinpricks, yet over the course of several weeks they had been making my world greyer, foggier, more airless. As a working mother, I had put my increasing difficulty concentrating down to fatigue; and if my heart sometimes beat a staccato rhythm in my chest, well, that was probably just stress.

The afternoon I went to A&E and was taken immediately through the curtained section Major Casualties, I sat on my trolley and tapped a work email on my iPhone. *It's probably nothing, but there's a possibility I might have a blood clot in my lung. I'm not sure I will be able to finish my Finals marking.* At the time, I was working for a major university and had a stack of exam scripts to mark. I couched my email apologetically, following it up the next morning with the confirmation of my diagnosis. I was – I hope accidentally – copied into the panicked email thread where there was a call to find a replacement for me, and I sent my husband out to post the exam papers special delivery at our own cost. Guilt lingering, shortly after I was discharged from the hospital I still agreed to sit on the examiners board, shakily making the 80-mile journey a few days later to sit in a stuffy room for two hours. That same week I presented at a major conference, even though the blood thinners I had been prescribed were making my gums bleed, my legs ache, and my period flow in a torrent that left me paranoid about staining my hotel bed.

None of this was tenable; that I assumed it would be was the result of a lifetime of grinning-and-bearing-it. I had learned to endure after years of my body being an inconvenience, a site of pain and fatigue. At 19 I had been scolded by a doctor for sobbing at the health centre reception desk because I was in so much pain from my period; the next year another doctor told me it would probably get better once I had a baby. Jump 13 years in the future, and – spoiler alert! – the pain did not lessen after I had my daughter, and the blood flow in fact got heavier. In the years between that tearful appointment and the birth of my child, I had tried a range of contraceptive pills and had a Mirena IUD fitted.

None of these interventions worked effectively enough to offset a range of unpleasant side effects, though the doctors I saw thought I should learn to live with them. *You just have to get used to it*, they implied, after weeks of nausea or bloating or mood swings. I went prepared for each new appointment, making sure I looked like a Professional Capable Woman, pushing hard to be heard. As my periods got heavier and more painful I did my own research, downloading dense medical journal articles and reading up on different contraceptive pills, learning the hormonal fingerprint of each one and learning about their use in clinical context. After scrupulous reading I was hopeful that one particular combined oral contraceptive (COC) pill called Eloine, containing a low dose of ethinylestradiol (oestrogen) with a progesterone (drospirenone) meant to very closely mimic the body's own hormone, would be less likely than anything else I'd taken to screw up my hormonal balance.

I was right. It worked. For a year my periods were light, mostly free of pain, and the side effects were minimal. It felt like a great weight had been lifted from my shoulders.

But then the Pill nearly killed me.

In 2012, a US Food and Drug Administration-funded study found that the use of drospirenone-containing pills caused a startling 77% rise in arterial blockages and blood clots compared to the use of other low-oestrogen pills. When I had asked my GP if the Eloine pill was suitable, he'd noted that it had a slightly higher risk factor than some pills for blood clots, but this risk had been presented to me as very small. He would check my blood pressure every three months instead of every six, and that had been that.

I hardly thought about it for the next 11 months or so until I found that my heart kept skipping a beat, the delayed pulse a hard shock in my chest. A creeping sense of dread sent me one afternoon not to my GP, but straight to A&E: a feeling strong enough to overcome my shrinking sense of embarrassment over making a fuss. Many of the symptoms of pulmonary embolism are easy to put down to stress or being run down: chest pain, dizziness, a cough. *I'm probably being silly*, I told the nurse who triaged me, *but...*

About 10% of pulmonary embolism cases cause sudden death.

For many people with a uterus, COCs relieve menstrual pain and bleeding, diminish PMS and PMDD, clear up acne. Oral contraceptives can dramatically improve quality of life. They can also end life, and I think the poor public awareness of the signs of PE is the extreme end of the scale that encourages women – and trans and non-binary folk with wombs – to put up and shut up, to bear physical and mental suffering as a natural by-product of their reproductive configuration.

Women (and people assigned female) in particular will often ignore all kinds of symptoms in the face of being too busy or too poor to take time off sick, or from the fear of not being taken seriously. Living in Britain, I benefit from a free national health service, and my job gave me paid sick leave. It's a lot easier to make the choice to go to a hospital if it won't cost you a thing. All the same, I almost didn't go; years of being told, more or less, to stop making a fuss about my periods had made me wary of being seen as another hysterical woman. It turns out quite a lot of women have died that way, blood clot travelling from the lung to the heart. Many of these deaths are marked as *sudden*; I wonder how many of those women were too tired and stretched thin to speak to a doctor about their symptoms, or who in a five-minute appointment with an overworked GP were told that their shortness of breath was probably due to anxiety, and they should try exercising more in the fresh air.

As late as 1981, *Time* magazine published a think piece on menstruation in which a family doctor was quoted as saying that many physicians saw menstrual pain as women's due. That was the year before I was born, and 12 years before I would start menstruating, but in my experiences with doctors since, I have certainly met a few who thought period pain was not only natural but inevitable: something to be endured, not eliminated. My monthly menstrual agony was classified as primary dysmenorrhea, period pain not caused by an underlying condition, and that seemed to move it for many doctors into a category of pain considered *natural*, as if *natural* means *does no harm*.

Following my pulmonary embolism, I wanted to get back to normal at once. It took me a while to realise that *normal* had contributed to the situation that let me skate perilously close to death. I had side-lined my own needs as I tried to juggle early parenthood within the exhausting environment of early-career academia, where every day I took off sick was a day closer to the end of my fixed-term contract: a day wasted in the publish-or-perish environment of modern academia, which wants us to pretend that the life of the mind is something separate from embodied experience. I had already strained against this expectation in my experience of pregnancy in 2015, when I had felt furious that the 'professionalism' demanded by the academy is of a type subtly but distinctively coded as white, middle class, and able-bodied male, that expects unruly bodies and messy emotions to be tucked away in a space marked *private life* without polluting the purity of the intellectual sphere. Two years later, newly aware of the fragile line between life and death, I no longer wanted to pretend that things were *business as usual*. Business as usual gets a lot of people killed.

I came off the Pill immediately after my blood clots were diagnosed, of course. My period returned with grim regularity, and my life-saving blood thinners meant the flow had become a torrent. In the minute between taking off my underwear and climbing into the shower, the floor beneath me would be stained red. This would go on for nine days at a stretch, and by the end I would feel hollowed-out, depleted.

In November 2017 I watched my inner arm purple with bruises after a nurse tried several times to draw blood. For someone with a surfeit of it elsewhere in my body, it has always been curiously hard to get into my veins. She succeeded at last, sending two vials away for tests as part of normal preoperative procedures. Feeling that I had come to the end of the line with my choices in managing my periods, I had opted for a more drastic solution: an endometrial ablation. Soon after those tests, I had the lining of my womb burned away, taking with it both my periods and the possibility of carrying another child.

I was happy – am happy – with having one child. All the same, that dull November day I swallowed hard against tears, feeling a physical ache of knowing what it had meant to be pregnant once and knowing I would never be again.

In the years since, my freedom from menstruation has been nothing but a relief, and I have never regretted that decision. Sometimes I think back to the 19-year-old woman weeping to an unsympathetic doctor – or even further back, to the 12-year-old girl who wrote in her diary how painful her recent period had been, and that *I hope it's not that bad again* – and wish I could tell them that one day that pain would be gone. But I would have to admit to them too how very many years of suffering still waited, and I am glad to leave them in the dark.

What next?

- **Thrombosis UK** (*thrombosisuk.org*) – Thrombosis UK works to increase awareness, support research and extend understanding through education and the sharing of information to improve care for all those affected by thrombosis.

mood swings and misunderstandings

the complexities of 'teenage hormones'

by Cathy Naughton

My FIRST SERIOUS relationship began when I had just turned 16. Twelve months later, my then-boyfriend and I were ready to go 'all the way'. The embarrassment of admitting to my mom that I had started having sex was soon overridden by the anxiety associated with using condoms as our only form of contraception. In Irish society, even in 2011, an unwanted pregnancy was by far the most shameful thing that could befall a teenage girl, and it would be another seven years until abortion was legalised in Ireland.

My mom made an appointment for me to see our local GP and would have to accompany me because I was under 18. The GP was a woman in her forties who I had met before; she exuded slightly more matter-of-factness than empathy, as I have found is common among doctors. She described the options for hormonal contraceptives that were available, and then very gently steered me towards a specific brand of the combined oral contraceptive pill (or often, simply 'the Pill'), suggesting that it was the least invasive method of contraception, relatively affordable, and 'a good place to start'.

The doctor then listed some of the possible side effects, including weight gain, acne, and mood swings. I was lucky that I had not yet experienced mood swings during my teenage years, despite the ever-fluctuating cocktail of strange hormones that had begun coursing through me since the onset of puberty. She advised that if I did experience any problematic side effects, I could simply stop taking the Pill and the side effects would soon dissipate. I was convinced, but I was also very impressionable on the subject, with little prior knowledge of the various alternatives' pros and cons. At the time, protected sex with a risk of side effects was significantly more appealing than sex with a higher risk of pregnancy.

Five years later while living in Edinburgh and studying for a master's, I was browsing online when I came across a *Guardian* article with the headline 'The pill is linked to depression – and doctors can no longer ignore it'. Before I had even clicked through to the full article, I felt an overwhelming sense of relief, or even vindication. I hadn't even read the piece yet, and already felt grateful towards the author for the strength and directness of the title. I felt understood in a way that would have made so much of a difference when I was 17.

The author, Holly Grigg-Spall, reported on a recently-published research paper describing a study undertaken at the University of Copenhagen. The findings identified a strong link between the use of hormonal contraceptives and diagnoses of depression. Of more than one million women who took part in the study, those who were taking the Pill were 23% more likely to be subsequently diagnosed with depression. Teenagers were shown to be at the greatest risk: those taking the Pill in their teens were 80% more likely to show symptoms of depression.

As a 22-year-old, I read through these statistics in awe and thought about my 17-year-old self – completely unaware of this particular risk and never having experienced depression before. I spent much of that same day wondering what I, at 22, would say to my 17-year-old self if I could go back to the day she was prescribed the Pill by her GP. Would I warn her about what lay ahead of her in the coming months and years? Would I tell her that sex – with anyone – wasn't worth what she would soon go through? Would I simply tear the prescription from her hand and throw it away without explanation?

Two weeks after I had started taking the Pill, I went back to see the doctor for a check-up. I told her that I had been feeling tense and on edge for the previous few days, but didn't seem to be experiencing any unusual physical symptoms. I asked if these anxious feelings were likely an emotional side effect of taking the Pill. The doctor was quick to dismiss me, explaining that mood-related side effects of taking the Pill were highly unlikely to manifest within two weeks of a first dose. She then pointed out that I had started back at school after the summer holidays that same week, and was more likely feeling the stress of starting into the senior cycle of the secondary school curriculum. This might have made more sense to me if the state exams hadn't been more than 18 months away at the time, but I nodded in agreement all the same. I wasn't struggling with homework and was attentive in class, so I wasn't consciously aware of feeling school-related stress. The most consistent source of stress for me at the time was trying to decide whether my hair looked better straightened or curled.

I reasoned that the doctor was an expert in medication and healthcare, which therefore gave her the ability to decipher my innermost feelings and understand my changing moods better than I ever could. At the time, I lacked the confidence to express my concern when disregarded by the doctor, or to listen to my instincts telling me that something wasn't quite right.

The following four months were a blurred emotional rollercoaster. The feelings of tension and anxiety that I had described to the doctor steadily worsened; some days, I was sullen and quiet at school, only to burst into tears once I had sat down in my mom's car when she picked me up in the afternoons. It felt as though Adele had written every sad song on her new album, *21*, especially for me. I also felt irritable but described myself as 'grumpy', in the same way adults often referred to teenagers who were trying hard to suppress (often justified) anger. A young person of my generation expressing anger openly was deemed ungrateful and untrustworthy; the remnants of Catholic Ireland simply could not condone such blatant expressions of emotion, particularly in young women, who should be demure and ladylike lest they be labelled troublemakers.

My relationships suffered as a result of my worsening mood swings. My parents had previously thought of me as level-headed and reasonable, but now seemed to find it difficult to engage with me when I might burst into tears at the slightest upset. A close friend made purposeful eye contact with me one day in response to a sullen one-word answer to her question and said, 'Cathy, I can't remember the last time I saw you *really* smile'. I was either energetic and restless around my boyfriend, or listless and easily annoyed by him, and rarely felt simply content in his company. Even in those moments, I knew that it was no fault of his own that I wasn't connecting with him as I had before – there was something wrong with *me*. My concerns about the possible side effects of the Pill had been dismissed so definitively by the doctor that I no longer considered that it might be at the root of my volatile moods – I had resigned myself to the fact that I was simply experiencing the effects of fluctuating 'teenage hormones', and doing a less than decent job at managing them. I didn't have an understanding of how the Pill was very directly altering my brain chemistry and hormonal balances.

The phrase 'teenage hormones' is common in popular culture, often used to describe emotional reactions of young people that adults have a hard time understanding. I have experienced, and noticed among peers, how young people's concerns are frequently dismissed as fleeting and therefore invalid, despite the fact that young people are experiencing constant waves of change both internally and externally that influence their views of themselves, their worlds, and their futures. 'Teenage hormones' is a cliché that is dismissive of the vast complexity of biological and chemical changes that young people experience for years following the onset of puberty. I look back now and wish that my doctor, other adults, and society in general had been supportive rather than dismissive, encouraging me to investigate the possible reasons for my emotions becoming so erratic, rather than labelling them with a cliché and hoping that things settled down of their own accord.

Five years later, reading Grigg-Spall's article in the *Guardian*, I did not expect to encounter a form of the teenage hormones cliché when looking into more information about the Danish research study. Disappointingly, I did. An article by Anna Almendrala for *Huffington Post* quoted an expert in psychiatry and gynaecology named Catherine Monk, who linked the high rates of depression among the Danish study's contraception-using teen participants with the likelihood of heartbreak following a first sexual relationship. Monk was quoted as stating that 'the link between love, sex, and feeling depressed is strengthened by the fact that the contraception-depression link was strongest in adolescents, those who are at the developmental stage where trying to find a romantic partner is paramount'. In contrast to the relief I felt at Grigg-

Spall highlighting the link between hormonal contraception use and depression in her article, I felt disappointed and misunderstood yet again reading Monk's comment. In my case, heartbreak didn't result in depression as Monks suggests; depression resulted in heartbreak.

My confusion and misery came to a head in late December when I was 17. I wanted off the rollercoaster of sadness and anxiety, and convinced myself that I needed to make a change in my life if I wanted to feel better. My confidence was at rock bottom, and I was hyper-aware of how my mood swings were causing my loved ones worry and concern. I really cared for my then-boyfriend, and he was as supportive as any teenager in a first relationship could be. I couldn't have expected him to understand what was going on in my head when I was struggling to understand it all myself. I felt that I was causing him unnecessary suffering with my dramatic mood swings, and that he would be better off without my near-constant negativity and upset. I broke up with him in the early afternoon on New Year's Eve, assuring him that we would both be happier in the long run. What followed for me was a three-month period of textbook depression; emotional numbness, no interest in socialising or pastimes, and trudging through the obligations of each day like a zombie.

At some point during these three months I stopped taking the Pill, simply because I no longer needed to take it for contraceptive purposes. In late March, I finally started feeling like myself again. I reconnected with my friends and family, and was looking forward to things for the first time since the previous autumn. I didn't take the contraceptive pill again, and although I did experience another episode of depression two years later, it is difficult not to associate this first miserable experience with the fact that I had been taking the Pill throughout.

From discussions with friends, peers, and strangers in the years that followed, I believe that the intense hormonal fluctuations I experienced in my teens are shared by many others. However, the issue also seems to be infrequently handled with the care and attention required to help young people form healthy relationships with the processes of their brains and bodies. While a young person might not have the life experience of adults or the specific knowledge of healthcare professionals, they have something else that is uniquely invaluable – they have an understanding of what it's like to be their own self. Only by truly listening to young people and valuing their contributions can adults hope to improve upon and inform understanding of young people's experiences. With encouragement and trust, young people can articulate their personal experiences of the sometimes tumultuous chemical and hormonal changes that affect their feelings, thoughts, and behaviours.

I have learned so much about my own body's hormonal processes, and about the findings of research into the emotional effects of the combined pill. I can now say that, given the chance, I would *not* go to great lengths to convince 17-year-old me not to take the Pill. Instead I would assure her that no one – neither well-intentioned adults nor doctors –

understands her internal experiences like she does. She doesn't know it just yet, but she can trust her instincts when confronted with external doubts.

What next?

- **Spun Out** (*spunout.ie*) – Spun Out's vision is to help create an Ireland where young people aged between 16 and 25 are empowered with the information they need to live active, happy, and healthy lives.

period, the end

by Sigrid Nielsen

MARILYN MONROE. JAYNE Mansfield. Sophia Loren. Gina Lollobrigida. Brigitte Bardot.

Almost everyone who grew up in the 1950s and 60s in America – and in many other countries as well – will remember the Hollywood actresses of those days. They were everywhere: on cinema posters, on TV, on the radio, in magazines, in everyday conversation.

They were tall and glamorous. Their figures were full and their voices were soft. They wore their hair long and it flowed over their bare shoulders.

They were the ideal of their times. They were 'natural' women. 'Real' women. *Feminine* women.

In the small town in central California where I grew up (about 2000 people lived there, mostly descendants of

Scandinavians), our world was very different from the world of film actresses. Everyone's behaviour, especially women's, was closely watched. Anything unconventional was long remembered. 'Oh, God!' was serious swearing.

Even if our town had had a cinema, most of my schoolmates wouldn't have been allowed to watch grown-up comedies and adventures like *Solomon and Sheba* and *Some Like It Hot*, featuring Lollobrigida and Monroe. But they were very real to people in the town anyway – part of a hologrammatic world where we could live larger lives.

In 1956, a film star called Grace Kelly married Prince Rainier of Monaco. The story was reported around the world. My friends in the neighbourhood were fascinated. One girl was thrilled picturing the wedding and I made a folded paper 'fortune-teller' for her, which offered different futures including a royal romance. I remember how she grinned and her eyes lit up when she lifted the right flap (after several tries). For a moment, it was all real.

What did the stars offer us, especially girls my age? I don't think it was just a fantasy of wealth or fame – we knew we weren't going to be singers or models – but in a few years we were all going to be *women*.

The films celebrated the female stars' power to attract – 'hormones', as it was called – to inspire sex and romance, change fates, make an American film actress into a princess, move life on.

Everyone seemed to love being reminded of these powers. 'Curvy' was the highest compliment. It was an allowable way to talk about hips and breasts, but it wasn't just about women's bodies. There were curvy clothes, curvy shop fronts, and curvy cars. McDonald's built their fortune on their drive-in restaurants flanked by two gigantic curves in glowing neon.

Behind the scenes, something more serious was happening. For most of the 1950s, scientific research took place that had nothing to do with the better known space and atomic weapons programmes. It was research into the primary female hormone: oestrogen. This research would one day produce the contraceptive pill and change society far more than any mission to the moon. But most people knew nothing about it, and I don't think most wanted to learn.

Oestrogen had been known by medical researchers for over a century, and first isolated around 30 years earlier. It's the primary female hormone, which begins to be produced by female bodies at puberty. It causes girls to mature sexually and become what was described then as 'more feminine'.[1]

If you believed the movies (and we preferred the myths to the facts), sexual maturity would be a good change. You would be grown up. You wouldn't become a princess, but you would have a life to call your own.

But there was little information about what was going to happen physically. I knew, vaguely, about what was sometimes called 'periods', sometimes called 'the curse', but usually not called anything.

I only remember hearing about it once in public – from a filmstrip produced for schools by a sanitary products company, the one which still dominates the market throughout the world.

The filmstrip showed a diagram with words like 'uterus' and 'fallopian tubes'. It explained that 'natural' women got pregnant, and that every month, the womb developed a lining made of blood and tissue in case that happened. If it didn't happen, the lining had to be shed, and that was called menstruation.

The filmstrip quickly went on to assure us that menstruation was nothing to worry about, and even while bleeding for a few days, we could swim, play tennis, or go dancing in strapless formals. What I remember most about it was the cartoon images of the lucky, active young women: they were drawn without feet. They danced like fireflies from pool to tennis court to party without ever touching the ground.

The time of the great change was approaching. You didn't have to wait to take part if you hadn't developed breasts yet. You could buy a 'training bra' – supposedly in order to get used to the feeling of the straps and the elastic at the back, but really to show you were soon to be a member of the club. When I went to summer camp, still counting down to the change, I discovered that some of my fellow campers were compiling a secret list, rating our counsellors (young women students) as MS or MF. This turned out to stand for 'most stacked' or 'most flat'. They named the counsellor at the top of the MF list with laughter and scorn. (No one said she had won the booby prize – meaning, in the slang of those days, that she was the big loser.)

It was when I came home from summer camp that the long-awaited event finally occurred. I had a bit of a shock when I found blood on my thigh – at first I thought I'd been cut – but help was at hand. My mother and I went out to buy a sanitary belt, made by the company which had created the dancing firefly filmstrip. The belt had plastic clips at the front and back, which held the long paper tails of the sanitary pad. (You could also use another product which was 'worn internally', but I gathered that was for married women.)

Both my parents congratulated me. It seems strange to me now that despite the deep unease around menstruation and sexuality, people in the 50s felt that the old taboos had been conquered and often said that no one should be embarrassed about 'the facts of life'. My parents saw my first period as a happy occasion – though 'women's things' were not supposed to be mentioned after that except when strictly necessary.

But soon I found out there was another side to being a 'real', 'natural', hormonal woman.

It started with the first period and then got worse as the months went by.

I'd had no idea that there could be anything painful about periods. But for me, at the worst, they were severely painful. I knew my period was coming in a few hours because I would feel strange, sluggish, and feverish, and then the ache would start.

There would be sharp pain. Dull pain. Then more sharp pain. It felt as if I had been stabbed. I sweated. I might vomit or have chills. At times the pain was bad enough to make me want to scream and yell.

There was no explanation for this. 'Sometimes girls go through it', was all I could find out. There were no books about it in the school library. If there had been any in the public library, they would have been in a locked case.

It's hard to remember what you were told by implication rather than in words – but from the beginning I understood that period pains were not a real illness and missing school, or anything else, because of them was not an option. So I had to slog through whatever I was doing, behaving as normally as possible.

The most severe pain might last a few minutes, come and go over several days, or last for hours. I was usually able to avoid any particular attention. This seems strange to me now. What was everyone thinking? If you brought it up you would receive a puzzled look and a flat 'Oh', which suggested you shouldn't say any more. Painful periods must have been as common then as they are now, but everyone seemed to feel that the best thing to do for the sufferer was to make as little fuss as possible.

The clothes of the time made things worse. American high schools didn't have official uniforms – their dress code was unofficial, but strict. (My best girlfriend dared to wear thick-soled shoes with laces, which drew taunts and open-mouthed stares.) The conventional straight skirts were tight in order to make a young woman's hips look wider. Undergarments were cumbersome – tights hadn't been invented. These weren't comfortable clothes to wear, especially if you were ill.

The illness had a medical name – dysmenorrhoea. Your clothes might make you feel worse, but there were over-the-counter products that promised they could make you feel better. One advert showed a sad teenager over the caption 'Sally's blue', and then a happy picture in pink: 'Sally's gay – with Midol'.

I tried everything, including Midol. It didn't make me gay. (That had already happened, though I didn't know it yet.)

Internet sites these days will tell you that painful periods can be a symptom of problems which need treatment. Anyone who has severe pain is advised to look for medical help.

No doctor I ever consulted in the 1960s said anything like this.

I saw our college physician when I was still having severe pain in my twenties and asked his advice. He said that when girls stayed single and didn't make use of their natural gifts, they could expect to have problems.

Of course, I didn't tell the doctor that I had never wanted children. (Still less did I tell him that I'd been in a relationship with my best friend with the unusual shoes for several years.) He may have felt that choosing to be childless, not period pain, was my real medical complaint. All women 'wanted' to give birth – it was their biological destiny. (Later a therapist gave me a book called *The Power of Sexual Surrender* which said that a woman who had not given birth was 'deeply defeated in life'.[2]) Defying your hormones would lead to trouble. Acceptance of your (supposed) nature was the only sure cure.

I accepted that I was paying the price for dissing Mother Nature. I agreed that I was unstable, immature, not normal. But, sure cure or not, I didn't want to create another life in order to have painless periods. I thought I would just have to give that idea a miss – how would I decide whether to name the baby Aspirin or Midol?

Other women at college suggested many less drastic period pain cures. Blackberry brandy. Heating pads. As the mid-60s and the counterculture dawned, going on the Pill. Cannabis. Herb tea.

My mother confessed that she too had had severe period pains. 'Sometimes', she admitted, 'I drank whisky'.

It was much later that I found out that whisky hadn't worked for my mother: her period pains, it turned out, had been even worse than mine. But she never told me how bad they had been until she was in her eighties. I don't know if this was because she just couldn't talk about menstruation, or if she felt the pain meant that something about her wasn't right.

Eventually I found something that did help the pain, at least sometimes: exercise. No one ever recommended it as a cure for period pain: I found out it helped accidentally, when I had to walk a long way to get to work.

Exercise is often mentioned on internet sites today, along with many other new suggestions. There is no shortage of other home remedies, but still, no certainty that any of them work. And in a way, recommending them implies that views haven't really changed – that period pains are not a real illness, just a nuisance. Period pain, says the NHS website,[3] is a common and a *normal* part of your menstrual cycle.

Even so, by the 1970s it began to seem that life was changing. The secret birth control research of the 1950s was having huge and unforeseen effects. The Pill was now legal for single women. Clothes were comfortable, and being a lesbian no longer shocked everyone all the time. Meanwhile, the Hollywood oestrogen goddesses were fading away one by one.

(Much more about the actresses – actors, we would call them now – emerged later. They were not just alluring bodies in shiny dresses. Gina Lollobrigida was a sculptor and journalist. Jayne Mansfield, supposedly the dumbest of the dumb blondes, spoke five languages. Marilyn Monroe, despite childhood poverty and abuse, perfected her acting talent – though she struggled with depression and in the end died by suicide. Another star, Hedy Lamarr, was an inventor whose work laid the foundations of Wi-Fi.)

In films and on TV, the new stars of the 1970s looked more individual, like Twiggy, Meryl Streep and Sally Field, or were outspoken about their political views, like Jane Fonda and

Barbra Streisand. Meanwhile a better way of life was taking shape for many people in our generation who had felt crazy and inadequate. We discovered the politics of change.

I joined a feminist consciousness-raising group and we talked about first sexual experiences – how we had bought into the romantic myths in the movies and how empty they had been for us. But we never talked about period pain.

Finally – later, when I had moved to Edinburgh in my thirties – I became involved in the lesbian, gay, and feminist book trades. I was in fairly good shape from hefting boxes of books, but I was still having bad period pains. We sold many books about women's health, but nothing seemed to address them.

There was some new information there, however, for those who wanted to find it. *Our Bodies, Ourselves*[4] was one of our most popular titles – a unique and innovative book about women's sexual and reproductive health. It included medical information but also interviews with ordinary women about their perception of their bodies and health needs. There was also an extensive resources list with warnings about books with a negative view of women.

The four pages (out of 592) on period pain in *Our Bodies, Ourselves* contained all the home remedies I had ever heard of and many more. It suggested that better medical understanding of period pains was now closer. But only in the section on endometriosis did it state emphatically that severe pain was a danger sign.

Perhaps this changing point of view convinced me that I should have one more try at going to a doctor and looking for some help, even though I guessed it would bring the same dismissive comments.

But this time, my GP didn't say 'Oh'. He didn't ask if I had tried paracetamol or ibuprofen. He didn't ask if I had been to see a therapist. He said:

'We have something that can help with that. It's called an anti-prostaglandin. Take it when you start to have pain'.

I was a bit surprised. I didn't ask what prostaglandins were. I took the prescription to the chemist and kept the pills until the pain started, which happened after a day-long bookstall at a conference in 1981.

I went to a cafe, ordered a coffee, and took the pill. Five minutes went by. Then the pain simply stopped. One second the pain was there, and the next second it wasn't. The heavy, sick, weak feeling that always came with the pain vanished as well. It was like walking through a door into another life.

I kept taking the pills, and the story of my period pain ended after 240 months.

By the time I reached my forties, the pain gradually became less and less, and I didn't need the pills any longer. I had an uneventful menopause. Mother Nature had clearly changed her attitude.

Thinking this story over, I had to wonder: has anything else changed? What is it like to cope with period pains today?

I assumed things must be much better for younger women

now – nearly sixty years after I had to handle the problem in isolation at age 13 with no resources except a school filmstrip.

Today a 13-year-old can look for help on the internet – though the quality varies and as with everything on the internet, caution is essential.

If you look for advice about period pains on the NHS webpage, it will explain that period pain is caused by prostaglandins, another hormone. Prostaglandins exaggerate the efforts of the womb to rid itself of the lining which builds up every month and cause the muscles to cramp painfully.[5] It recommends that you try over-the-counter painkillers, or if they don't work, go to your GP for something stronger. You can also try a heating pad or exercise, or a shower, massage, relaxation techniques, or a device which delivers a mild electrical current to stimulate your nerves and relieve the pain.

Another site, verywellfamily.com, provides detailed descriptions of severe versus more usual symptoms – even a poster-like sheet of illustrations, which might help make the point clear to someone, like a 13-year-old who is unfamiliar with medical advice.[6]

Other sites offer the familiar remedies and some new ones – taking painkillers before your period starts,[7] drinking more water,[8] cinnamon,[9] and more. All advise anyone with severe period pains to be checked out for underlying causes other than prostaglandin. Another site mentions emotional symptoms as part of dysmenorrhea – low moods, meaning depression (or feeling crazy).[10]

Others mention drugs called Non-Steroidal Anti-Inflammatory Drugs or NSAIDs – possibly the anti-prostaglandin medication I was prescribed. Some of these drugs include diclofenac, ibuprofen and naproxen. NSAIDs, says the site, work for some people, but can have serious side effects.[11] One article suggests that views about the best use of these drugs for treating period pain are changing all the time.[12] A great deal remains to be learned about the reasons there can be so much grief in one of the basic processes of life.

I hope no one will accept what these websites say uncritically. The internet offers a huge range of information, some reliable, some not. Still, these websites offer hope. They offer information without encouraging self-blame.

But self-blame about menstruation is still very real. In telling this story I've realised how fortunate I have been, over my lifetime, to leave a restrictive life behind and find a different home in the world. But the obstacles on that journey are now clearer to me as a negative force than they were before I did this research. I don't think the feminism of my time addressed it. We assumed these attitudes would gradually improve as ignorance about women receded.

Yet, two years ago, the *Independent* published a study which suggests that over half of women consider menstruation a painful, shaming subject. They say they would go to almost any length to avoid mentioning menstrual blood or periods.[13]

It doesn't take much research to discover many more articles like this – for instance, one from Australia, which quotes researcher Dr Carla Pascoe of Melbourne University. She found that many women struggle to talk about menstruation even with family or partners.[14]

Meanwhile, a study by the UN Population Fund goes further – it reported that, in many parts of the world, anti-menstrual stigma is a serious threat to women. It threatens their rights and sometimes their lives.[15] It is not a fading remnant of ignorant times.[16] It is misogyny. It needs to be called out and challenged much more strongly than we've ever done before.

Sixty years of learning, understanding the power of the myths, and linking with each other are a good beginning.

What next?

- **Our Bodies Ourselves** (*ourbodiesourselves.org*) – Our Bodies Ourselves is a global project aimed at publishing content that empowers women with information about health, sexuality, and reproduction. They work in and build bridges among social justice movements.

what if i'm not just a massive bitch?

by Heather Parry

In 1931, French philosopher Jean-Paul Sartre set about an act of self re-definition: he was to become a novelist. The resulting book, *Nausea*, is a quintessential existentialist novel; the protagonist, a former adventurer named Roquentin has settled, like Sartre, in Normandy, and begins to feel things outside of his control; he is disgusted by a wet rock; no, he decides, he is afraid of it. Over the four weeks of the novel, Roquentin comes to realise that the issue is the things and people around him; the way they, and the rest of the real world, place him within its context:

> *I have never before had such a strong feeling that I was devoid of secret dimensions, confined within the limits of my body, from which airy thoughts float up like bubbles. I build memories with*

my present self. I am cast out, forsaken in the present: I vainly try
to rejoin the past: I cannot escape.

The vast totality of the world around Roquentin limits his inability to define himself in the way he wishes; it encroaches on his 'being'; he is nauseated. And yet, in this world he is trapped. Recognition of the material and metaphysical conditions in which we live is core to Sartrean existentialism; for the rest of his life Sartre will write about the ways we can try to reach authenticity, the process of having a 'true and lucid consciousness' of our own situation as humans, within which we assume all the risks and responsibilities of our absolute freedom and define ourselves regardless. This, for Sartre, is the goal: to recognise our reality, and forge forwards within it, taking responsibility for everything we do along the way.

At the end of *Nausea*, Roquentin resolves to write a novel, and with this work he hopes that he will be able to look back on his life, on himself, 'without repugnance'; he knows that he will never free himself from the nausea of existence, but he dreams that he 'might succeed – in the past, nothing but the past – in accepting [him]self'.

I am 17 years old when, like feminist existentialist icon Simone de Beauvoir before me, I fall in love with Jean-Paul Sartre. Unlike de Beauvoir, I discover Sartre not on a course at the École normale supérieure in Paris, but in a sixth-form classroom in Rotherham, amongst several boys unironically wearing berets and floor-length leather jackets.

I take to Sartre like a duck to water. The things he writes about – morality, responsibility, freedom, the sheer pain of existing – are the sorts of lofty concerns to which I aspire, and they have a certain Parisian glamour, the sort of thing that an unquiet girl from a former mining town imagines herself discussing over vermouth on a Paris evening, despite not knowing what vermouth is or having ever been to Paris.

At 17 I am restless and largely ungrateful; I have been taught to have faith in my own understanding of a situation, meaning that I go around rules and think I know better. I have never worried about being fed or housed, I have been encouraged in anything I might want to do, and any pain I have known has been mitigated by unconditional love. I am privileged and I do not know it, and all my privileges – a caring family, a safe home, rules meant to stop me from making bad choices – I find constricting, enraging, annoying. I am, in short, a Bitch.

It's around this time that I will catch my mother staring at me, in the loving and concerned way that mothers stare at their children as they awkwardly turn from child to adult, and I will snap *What?*, to which she will respond, with a sigh, *You used to be so lovely*.

In the dozens of times I've told this anecdote, I have presented this as hilariously cutting; funny, that my own mother would say such a thing to me; how end-of-the-pier sharp; how curiously Northern. Yet even at the time I knew that she was right. I *had* been lovely, a weird little buttery flapjack of a kid with a turned up nose and an open mouthed laugh whose skin condition meant she had to be wrapped tightly in bandages at night, drawing wild sympathy from everyone with eyes. I sang loudly and badly. I kissed every member of my family and each of my teddies before I went to sleep. I had a go at everything that might quell my energy (figure skating, hockey, double gymnastics classes on Friday night), my chubby thighs packed into a whole array of badly fitting and highly flammable uniforms and costumes. I was strange but I *was* lovely. And I am distinctly *not* lovely at 17 years old. I am a tornado of impatience and irritation and focused hatred; I don't sleep well, and I spend my nights watching 80s horror B-movies on Channel Four. I am sullen and pissy at home, I have painted my walls blood red in an act of comical teenagerness and though I don't tell anyone, I often feel completely numbed to the outside world, quite literally incapable of feeling a feeling, which I deal with by the time-honoured method of lying on my bedroom floor with the curtains closed listening to Nirvana. I have periodic bursts of uncontrollable rage in response to, for instance, returning from a Saturday out to find that someone has tidied my things. The anger will be a physical response, my hands shaking, my heart racing, my nails digging into my palms, my teeth biting deep into my lips, and it will only dissipate with an outburst, only by the release of tearing up my room or smashing something of my own that won't be replaced. I am a black hole of a mood, a spitting cat. In these moments, I am confined within the limits of my body; within it is a violence that cannot get out and yet must. I cannot escape it; it has to come out.

It does not occur to me, at 17, that these overwhelming episodes of angry mania might have something to do with my endless outbreaks of bad skin, my ten-day periods or my inability to sleep. It doesn't register that the tension in every muscle or the blank numbness could be related to a menstrual cycle that seems to follow no rules, sometimes running at three weeks and sometimes five, or that my intense irritability may be explained by something within me, outside of my control. I don't connect these things to cramps, the bloating, the migraine so bad it left the entire left side of my body without feeling, making me think I, a teenager, was having a stroke. The fact that all this has happened in the four years since I first got my period does not click. I think all these things simply make up who I am: impatient, quick to anger, negative, resentful, mean. A Bitch.

A year later, I graduate from college and move to Manchester to study Philosophy and English Literature. At the end of that degree, I give a dismissive tattooist twenty pounds for him to tattoo me, badly, with the words from *Nausea: Je ne peux pas m'échapper*: I cannot escape. It is the choice of an overly earnest philosophy graduate with a high level of pretension and equal amounts of emo tendencies. But it's also, a little bit, an attempt to accept who I am, with all its many faults and sharp edges. To recognise the reality of myself.

Apart from a brief and unsuccessful dalliance with the Pill, I didn't even consider hormonal birth control until I was 24.

I heard about the contraceptive implant from my friend, Dr Zoe, who on a trip to the Czech Republic waxed lyrical about the ways in which it had improved her life. I was convinced enough by the idea that I would be able to forget about potential pregnancies entirely for three years, so quickly went to my local medical centre and got my upper arm injected with a thin rod of plastic containing enough progesterone to keep me child-free for 36 months. Apart from regular spotting and a fairly huge mood surge a few days after implantation – during which I cried and screamed and argued with my boyfriend – the implant worked for me just fine. So three years after that, I had my arm sliced open, had the rod pulled free from the tissues that had grown around it, and had another one jabbed right in.

The body's reaction to the implant is difficult to predict, much like the Pill – but unlike the Pill, to which your reaction will usually stay consistent, your body's response to the implant can vary each time, even to the exact same brand. My second implant unexpectedly changed my life for the better: it turned off my menstrual cycle entirely and rid me of all the things that came along with it. No bleeding, no PMS, no moods. I was chilled, more compassionate, able to concentrate; I did not bloat massively; I was not angry. My skin was the best it had ever been. There was no lip-biting, fist-clenching rage; no punching, no smashing. And though at the time I attributed it to a new partner, I was sleeping. I closed my eyes at night and woke up in the morning. I was nourished, I was calm, I was balanced. No longer did I feel 'confined within the limits of my body'. I felt like an entirely different – and a wholly better – person.

Over the next three years, many of my friends would ask me some variation on the following: *but doesn't it make you feel disconnected from your body? Don't you miss having your period? The answer was always: no, not in the slightest, are you absolutely mad?* I couldn't believe that amenorrhoea (the lack of a period) was listed as a *dis*advantage of the implant on the NHS website. I felt very strongly that I had been freed from the ludicrous burden of menstruation, and attributed the strange reaction of my friends to the fact that, having lived with their periods for close to two decades, they were suffering from some sort of collective amnesia about what Life Before Periods was actually like. It didn't occur to me that perhaps their PMS didn't completely dictate their actions, their reactions, how they fundamentally defined themselves as people.

Jean-Paul Sartre's existentialism is rooted in personal responsibility; you, a human being, are condemned to be free, in that you are brought into the world, and before you lies everything you might ever choose to do, and into this deluge of choice you are thrown. There is no God to guide you; there is no human nature upon which you may build. There is you, alone, in the horrifying everything, and you must invent yourself as you go, taking responsibility for every choice that you make. Every possibility is open to you.

No; it is not *every* possibility; it is *almost* every possibility. There is an existentialist concept that does a lot of the heavy lifting in the process of turning Sartrean existentialism from an academic theory into an applicable life philosophy: facticity. These are the concrete facts of your life; where you were born, who your parents were, your height, your eye colour, your physical condition. Facticity represents the unchangeable; the things you cannot escape.

Existentialism accepts facticity as a limit on freedom, but it does not accept it as an absolute limit. Facticity represents the hand you have been dealt, but not the choices you make in reaction to it. Within the confines of facticity, you are still free to make yourself who you wish to be, and responsible for every part of that.

My implant, of course, ran out after three years. I had it replaced, and my body decided to turn tail on me, just when I thought we'd made a pact. Friends found it hilarious how devastated I was when I started to sporadically bleed again; truth be told, I was being highly melodramatic. But over the next eighteen months, it felt I was regressing a decade and a half. I was moody, restless, tense; my skin was bad, my concentration was shot, my head ached, I bled for five days, ten days, twelve days. Two years and two months after having the new implant, I was left with the full experience of my natural hormonal state: for the ten days preceding my period I could not sleep, waking up an average of ten times in the night, sweating and exhausted, never able to reach the REM state wherein your body actually rests. By the end of the ten days I would be incapable of properly thinking;

then, a fourteen-day period. My skin broke out seemingly at random, my self-focused anxiety (newly procured) was so bad I didn't want to leave the flat and I found myself having wild and pointless arguments with my partner, at the end of which I would burst into tears and be inconsolable for hours, not wanting to even be touched. I felt bitter, intolerant, bitchy; all of that felt out of my control, something I could only even identify in retrospect. Who was that person? Why was she back?

It was a Monday in September when I realised none of this was normal. I was consumed with rage; I could not think of anything other than how angry I was. I ground my teeth, I dug my nails into my palms, I literally shook with rage. I did a workout to try to shake it off; nothing. I lifted weights heavier than I could usually manage; still my hands shook. It didn't stop until I went into the spare room, looking for something breakable but not expensive, and kicked the shit out of the plastic clothes rack until my washing was everywhere and my legs hurt. Fifteen years were wiped off my life in a second; I am seventeen, I am bewildered by rage, I am a spitting viper. I have done something stupid and pathetic that inconveniences only me. I am that person all over again.

The next day I got my period, and the blindingly obvious finally fell into place; it was my hormones making me into this person. The rage was not a personal failing, it was outwith my control. The intense irritability, the bitterness, the negativity – it was all on a cycle. My mother, it turned out, had experienced the same, hers taking the form of insomnia, blinding migraines and surges in temper. The sleeplessness was not a hangover from a childhood of bad nights; it was part of my hormonal response. I could tolerate it at seventeen; in my thirties, it wrecked me completely. This whole situation was thanks to my own body; this person was part of me. These were the concrete facts of my life; these actions of mine were defined by this. Who I was – it was defined by this. I was back to who I was before, but without the cushion of youth to protect me. *I am rejected, abandoned in the present.*

There are subtle differences in the various English translations of *Nausea* from the original French, meaning falling between the cracks of language as it tends to do. In one, the phrase I had tattooed on my back – *je ne peux pas m'échapper* – is not just rendered as 'I cannot escape'. The *m'* implies that the escape is personal, it is from something. It is from you, the person speaking. *I cannot escape from myself.*

In this translation, what Roquentin has to make peace with is the man that he is, here, in this present moment, in response to the world around him – and within him.

I am 32 years old when I go to a doctor and tearily tell her about what is happening to me. She misunderstands; I am not complaining about my hormonal birth control. I do not want to change it. I am relying on my hormonal birth control and it is not working as I need it to. There is no guarantee that with a new implant my symptoms will be quelled again; there is no certainty that I will become the (relatively) calm lake of water I briefly was. But that is who I think I am, when the influence of my wild hormones is mitigated, and it's who I wish to be again. So she takes my implant out early, and I get a new set of miniature scars on my upper left arm. Whether it works or not, I will still have to contend with that worst version of myself; she might be sent away, but it won't be forever. The work I have to do remains. But, still, I watch the rod being injected into the fatty part of my arm, and I cross my fingers.

In 15 years or thereabouts, my body will begin a whole new round of changes. I will exist in a whole new maelstrom of hormonal response, and it may well be awful. I will, no doubt, have to re-define myself yet again, looking in a 'true and lucid' manner at my behaviours and feelings, seeing once again if they are out of my control and how this affects the version of me that I seem to be. There's no escaping the situation, the way my body acts; this is my concrete reality for the next two decades. It is, on some level, who I am – or at least a small part of it. Perhaps I will get a brief respite – and if not, there are other ways to work with the limitations I have. Regardless, I know now that my worst self is not the totality of who I am. The thing I cannot escape from is not the world; it is myself, a part of me, the experience of myself and all the things that come with it. But in that knowledge I might succeed – in the past, but also in the present, and maybe even in the future – in accepting myself. With a little hormonal help.

What next?

- **International Association for Premenstrual Disorders**
  (*iapmd.org*) – The International Association for
  Premenstrual Disorders provides support for anyone
  impacted by the core premenstrual disorders:
  Premenstraul Dysphoric Disorder and Premenstraul
  Exacerbation of underlying disorders.

'wait. i'm not finding a heartbeat'

by Laura Pearson

I WOKE IN the dark. My chest was slick with sweat, my hair and pyjamas sticking to me. For a moment I lay there breathing, wakening, taking in the darkness. I reached a hand inside my top, peeled the wet material away from my body and invited the cooling air onto my skin. Initially I mistook the growing anxiety in my chest as the result of a feverish dream, and then as my brain awoke, the memories flooded my mind. My throat tightened, tears welled, and I let my hard sobs release quietly, trying not to wake my husband as my body shook with grief. My unborn baby had died. It wasn't a nightmare after all. These night sweats had woken me all week and thrown me into a dark, lonely tunnel of grief – stealing my sleep, leaving me exhausted and drained.

I pulled myself out of bed to the bathroom and sighed as I pulled down my pyjamas and saw the fresh blood in my pants. 'Go away', I sobbed quietly in our bathroom, 'just go away'.

My body had just delivered a baby, but we were now dealing with the aftermath of labour without my newborn. I didn't have my baby to nurse to help my uterus shrink and reduce the bleeding. I had no newborn for skin-to-skin contact to provide me with much needed oxytocin, to help me relax, lower my stress and anxiety. I was having night sweats and relentless mood swings. And on top of all this, I was grieving. My mind was stuck on a loop, repeating the moment that changed everything – the moment in the hospital at our routine 20-week scan when the sonographer said, 'Wait…' It's that word that gets me. That single word that stole my smile, my hope, and my breath. 'Wait. I'm not finding a heartbeat'.

The process of what followed seems hazy to me. I remember reassuring the apologetic sonographer, who looked about seven or eight months pregnant herself. She said she couldn't do any more and they shuffled me, my husband and two-year-old son down the corridor to another room. The midwife there seemed flustered, not sure what to do. They sent us to another hospital for a second opinion. There they confirmed there was definitely no heartbeat. I had cried the whole way in the car, but I had already accepted that the second opinion wouldn't bring good news.

The conversation turned to getting 'the baby out'. The midwives explained I would take a pill there and then to get things started overnight, but I was allowed to go home and pack a bag. They couldn't tell me how long labour would take once they started me on the drugs. I was terrified I would start to deliver the baby at home, but they reassured me this was unlikely to happen. I think I lay awake the whole night. I stroked my belly and whispered to my baby when my husband fell asleep. They'd said at the second scan that they thought the baby had been dead for a few weeks. I keep questioning why my body had not even tried to push the baby out from within. As though, like me, it wanted to hold on, refusing to accept this as truth.

I returned to the hospital early in the morning, leaving my son and husband at home. We determined that our son needed love, normality, and routine after the chaos of the day before, so we put his needs first. I was on my own. I didn't want a friend or family member with me to worry about; I just wanted to do this on my own. It was less than 24 hours since I had been told my baby was dead. I think I was still in shock. I was given a pessary when they settled me in my room and told me I would need to take pills every three hours to force my body into labour. I was in a special bereavement suite that I later learnt was paid for by Fife Sands to be used by families in the same position as us. On the wall was a beautiful mural which strangely held a deep meaning for me. It was equipped with a fridge, refreshments, toiletries and, perhaps most importantly, it was at a decent distance from the other rooms in the maternity ward from which I might hear the first cries of newborns. The midwives were wonderful. One offered to sit with me the whole time, but I asked for some space and they were respectful and attentive, checking on me regularly. I was given an information pack of materials I might want to read. I read a book I had brought with me instead. Denial. I tried to doze, tried to watch TV, cried excessively and noisily and waited for the pain to come.

When it started, I was sick numerous times, curling up on the floor beside the toilet, then pacing the room, curling into a foetal position on the bed. Contractions became intensely painful. Crying, I asked for morphine – no need to limit my drugs since they could not harm the baby. I lay on the bed feeling myself float under a cloud. I rang my buzzer. 'The baby is coming', I shouted as the midwives opened the door. I felt his head pushing on me and the midwife told me to push when I felt the urge. Baby arrived. A little boy, they told me. Maybe it was the morphine or maybe those incredible maternal hormones, but I don't remember crying. I remember smiling and saying, 'Hello. You are so, so beautiful', and feeling absolutely overwhelmed with love for this tiny red person. His tiny lips were miniature versions of his big brother's. He was deathly still as I held him in my palms. He was, and will always be, my son. Sleeping, peaceful, beautiful.

I returned home to my husband, without our youngest son. He held me and I cried. Big heaving sobs. We named our beautiful baby as we sat in our living room holding hands. We had picked two boys' names and my husband encouraged me to pick my favourite. Then I snuck upstairs and climbed into bed with my older son. I watched his beautiful face as he slept, and my heart swelled with love as I realised how lucky I was to have him. But how sad I was he'd never meet his brother.

I didn't want to be apart from my toddler son in the early days after our loss. My love for him grew massively and he became my shining light, giving me a reason for getting up each day and keeping going. He felt like a precious gift. But it was exhausting. Playing his games, going to his groups and classes, smiling and being okay. Every evening I was emotionally exhausted. Gatherings of people were extremely difficult. I felt like I was acting the whole time when I just wanted to scream and shout, 'My baby is dead. I can't keep doing this small talk bullshit'. Holding that in, faking smiles and interest in mundane topics, remembering to concentrate when my thoughts were dragging me under, fighting the tears threatening to spill down my cheeks, just took so much energy and I became exhausted. I stopped going to one of the toddler groups because it was too painful seeing the new babies being passed about for cuddles and hearing good natured moans about tiredness and lack of sleep. I was exhausted without my baby and would have given anything to be tired because I was awake all night with him in my arms, not because of my nocturnal tears and night sweats.

I had a spiritual outlook on the miscarriage which I found brought me comfort and love. I was trying to accept my anger and the circumstances as part of a wider experience. But I just felt sad, so, so sad. It felt so hard to move forward when each time I went to the toilet and saw the blood still flowing from my body. I felt broken, wrong, my body unable to do the most basic things it should be able to do instinctively. Grow a baby, regulate periods. I felt like I had let my husband and son down. That I had failed in my job to keep our baby safe and well until he was ready to be born. I felt jealous when women told me it never even crossed their mind that they wouldn't have their baby after getting their positive test. It made me feel like there was something wrong with me. All these other women in my life made it all seem so easy. Get pregnant, have a baby. Sometimes by mistake. Shame and self-loathing dominated my thoughts while I tried to carry on as normal. But I chose the people I wanted to confide in, the ones who would allow me to wear my vulnerability openly, and as we talked, I watched our friendships strengthen.

The bleeding didn't stop as they told me it would, so after four weeks or so, I visited my GP. She got me a quick referral to the Gynaecological unit at the hospital where I had delivered both of my sons. They sent me for an ultrasound scan to check if there was any placenta left behind in my uterus that was causing the bleeding and intermittent pain I was experiencing. As I walked into the department, eyes raw and sore from weeks of crying, the lady on reception asked how many weeks pregnant I was and if I had an appointment with a midwife booked for after my scan. I managed to squeeze out 'No, I've been sent by gynae. I lost my baby" before the tears ate my words. She looked mortified. I felt surrounded by silence, open mouthed pregnant women and their oblivious partners on mobile phones. It felt like people were pulling back from me in case baby loss was something they might catch.

The scan showed nothing untoward so I was prescribed a course of hormones which would stop the bleeding. I wasn't keen to use them, but I didn't want to let this bleeding break me, and it didn't seem like my body was going to stop on its own. During the course I started to bleed again, which shouldn't have happened, so I stopped taking them. I went for Reiki and started taking supplements, slowly my periods regulated and I started to find my new normal.

It's lonely losing a baby. Probably any bereavement feels a bit like that. Alone with this huge heart full of love you have for the one who is lost. But losing an unborn child felt different somehow. No one had met him or even seen him. We weren't willing to share photos of him, and in a way he felt invisible. We were given a funeral for him, with costs covered by the NHS and a local funeral director. We saw his tiny coffin; we collected his ashes in a cardboard tube. We got his name inscribed on a stone in the crematorium, which helped me feel he is real, recognised by society as someone. A real person I can grieve for. But I think there are still many who don't understand, who see him as a foetus, not a baby. Wondering how I can be so sad for this loss when I never had him in the first place.

And I think it feels different because of that. Because I have no memories, nothing to smile about when I talk to others about him. No shared laughter about something he said or did. All I can say is he was beautiful. He was a baby, my baby, our baby. He was potential, a life unwritten, he was a son, a brother, a nephew, a grandson, a friend. He was a gift, a miracle and the sadness will be ever present for me, not having the chance to watch him grow up. Knowing he will be static, a Peter Pan boy, freeze-framed in death. More than anything I want people to acknowledge him, his birthday, his name, his existence and give me time and space to talk about him. As they would do with any other child, one who was lucky enough to be born with a beating heart and air in his lungs.

What next?

- **Fife Sands – Stillbirth and Neonatal Death Charity** (*fife.sands.org.uk*) – Fife Sands is a volunteer-led group that supports families through the pain and grief of losing a baby. The organisation works with local healthcare professionals to promote access to Sands' material and training to raise awareness about stillbirth and neonatal death to help break the silence about this tragedy.

the puberty that wasn't supposed to exist

by Maya Posch

GROWING UP IS something that most children look forward to – to no longer be seen as a 'child' or be held back by age restrictions. Becoming a teenager and going through puberty almost feels like a special initiation ceremony, with fact and rumour mingling as the older children discuss among themselves what they'll be facing.

I remember the 'your body during puberty' books that we had access to during primary school, with crude drawings of the male and female body. These books described how our bodies would transform into either form, depending on what genitals we were born with. Growing up in the Netherlands, there wasn't a feeling that one should be ashamed of this process, nor be ashamed of having genitals.

And so I perceived puberty as something that I'd be glad to go through, as another step in the process of becoming a grownup. What actually happened to me, however, was beyond confusing and defied everything that I had read or been told about puberty.

My expectation was that I would find myself going through a male-style puberty, on account of having been born with the required 'dangling bits' – the explosion of body and facial hair, the breaking of the voice and a host of other changes. But my voice never did break, and the facial and body hair never made it past a serious fuzz. This was mildly confusing, to say the least.

What was also unusual was that I had a sudden beginning of breast growth when I was eleven years old, and an episode of severe abdominal cramping that had me basically unable to walk and move for at least an hour. When my parents found me during that episode, my dad had to carry me downstairs while my parents prepared to get me to the local doctor.

Unfortunately, by the time that we got to the doctor, the pain had subsided and instead of an examination I got a pat on the head and was returned home. There, my dad told me that he didn't appreciate it if I faked being in pain just for attention. This warning really stuck with me and, for the coming years, every time I experienced discomfort or pain in the abdomen or perineum, I would ignore it.

As I watched my fellow students during primary school and onward transform into 'regular' teenage guys and girls, I felt only more confused and lost. I knew on some level that my body wasn't following either of those courses, but I found myself unable to put it into words. My body definitely was changing, but it seemed to want to neither transform into a man or a woman, putting only a halfhearted effort into either direction.

Unable to do anything with this observation, I put it to the side and just tried to live my life. This turned out to be a pretty miserable experience, with my environment also struggling to make sense of what was happening to my body. As I moved through puberty, I got identified as a young woman instead of a young man more and more frequently, with some people bluntly asking me whether I was a woman or a man. This seemed to be due to my physical appearance not matching up to my male clothing and male haircut. When I let my hair grow out by the end of high school – ironically, to look tougher as a guy – I ended up being seen only as a woman.

It would take many more years after finishing high school before I was able to put a name to these experiences. While struggling through conflicting feelings about my body and how I should behave, I became aware of myself trying to appear to others like a woman rather than a man. This confused me, leading me to consider the question of whether I felt like, or wanted to be, a man or a woman. It had become clear to me that ever since puberty began, I had not tried to 'pick a side', so to say.

Initially, this led me to believe that I was transsexual, as this was the only thing that I knew of at the time that would make me want to be a woman when I was so obviously male. Yet within a week, I had come across a new term: 'intersex', with a whole range of body configurations and medical terms accompanying it. Remembering all my confusion and troubles with my body over the years, I began to suspect that I might be a true hermaphrodite, with both male and female stem cells and reproductive organs.

Going from a theory about one's body and finding the medical attention that would help to either prove or disprove that theory turned out to be much more complicated than I had thought. While I managed to get into contact with the largest gender team in the Netherlands at the VUmc hospital, they didn't seem excited about my 'intersex' theory.

They supposedly ran a hormone level test on a blood sample and told me that I had normal male hormone levels. Their gynaecologist prodded and poked at me for a bit and told me that he saw no sign of me being intersex. Their psychologists kept asking me why I was even there if I was not ready to admit to being transsexual, since I clearly wasn't intersex.

There were a few years of this, with an intermission at a psychiatrist who, during the first appointment, told me that I was deceiving myself about being intersex. They later told me that I should just pretend to be transsexual at the gender team to get the surgery and hormone therapy. At the last psychologist appointment with the VUmc gender team, all previous promises were withdrawn about speeding up the protocol. Something broke inside of me.

I cancelled all of my outstanding appointments at the VUmc gender team, and left the hospital to find my own path instead.

A few months later, I had an MRI scan performed at a German private clinic. This was my first MRI scan ever, and when I sat next to a flabbergasted and very excited radiologist shortly afterwards, it felt like vindication in so many ways. As the radiologist pointed out the closed-off vagina in my abdomen and the non-existent prostate, it felt like the first time that a medical professional had been truly honest with me.

That same year I had also begun hormone therapy, because I felt that pushing my body towards the development of further female secondary characteristics made the most sense. I had to order these hormones via the internet because I had no doctor who would prescribe them to me. With grudging support from my local GP to have blood tests performed, I was able to deduce the dose of testosterone blockers and estradiol needed to get a female hormone balance. This also gave me a first glimpse into my true, natural hormone balance: my testosterone levels were less than twenty-five percent of the lower range of male levels, and estradiol levels low for a woman, but high for a man.

With things seemingly headed in the right direction, I passed the MRI findings to my GP which led to them being sent to the VUmc gender team. However, they concluded that they could see no unusual anatomy on the MRI images. Following this were a few more years of back and forth between Dutch hospitals and multiple MRI scans being made with inconsistent results.

One Dutch specialist diagnosed me as suffering from autoparagynaecophilia, the delusion of thinking that I look female, when in fact I do not. During the appointment leading up to that conclusion a female urologist was invited in to help examine me. Her first words when she saw me upon entering the room were: 'She really does look like a girl!'

During all of the years that I had visited hospitals, there was always the point where I found myself sitting in the waiting room, with a call out for a 'Mr Posch', followed by a stammering and confused assistant trying to make sense of their expectations and what their eyes were telling them. Back around 2008, I had managed to get my official name changed from my original male name to the new, female name. The judge found no flaw with the argument and photograph of me supplied by my lawyer, approving the name change based on my female appearance.

This of course did not fix the confusion around my appearance when my official gender came into play, as illustrated by the constant humiliations in waiting rooms. Making no progress with getting any sensible answers out of medical professionals, I decided that maybe changing my official gender was easier. For this, Dutch law required that I had to have both testicles removed.

Since doing so (elective orchiectomy) was not allowed under Dutch law, I found a willing German surgeon via a transsexual friend. This surgeon performed not only the orchiectomy, but also did an exploratory surgery of the perineum, during which he confirmed the entrance of a vagina. Lacking the skills to perform the reconstructive surgery required to affix the vagina to the perineum, he closed it back up. The biopsy on the removed testicles showed that they were largely undeveloped, which explains why they produced only small amounts of testosterone.

The resulting letter from this surgeon allowed me to file to have my official gender changed, using a neverbefore-used Dutch law from the 1980s that allows intersex people who were born with both types of genitals to take on their preferred gender. Like with my name change, this all happened without any hearing and this lawyer too was surprised how easily it went. The case even got Dutch media attention, with a national broadcaster dropping by to hold an interview for the news and a number of newspapers reporting on it.

As far as the Dutch medical professionals went, they kept denying that I could be intersex, and that was that.

I eventually moved to Germany, where after a few years I began to notice some curious changes to my body, including a vertical brown stripe (linea nigra) on my abdomen that is mostly associated with pregnancies. With assistance from a doctor at a local medical centre, it was determined that the problem was that my body had begun to produce more female hormones, which together with the (low-dosed) estradiol hormone therapy I was taking was causing me to suffer an estradiol overdose.

After terminating the hormone therapy completely, the linea nigra vanished after a few months and I was free of the hormone therapy which I had assumed I would be on for the rest of my life. Instead, I now seem to have a natural, regular female hormone cycle.

In addition to this, I also noticed a continuation of the development of female secondary characteristics, most noticeable with my breasts as I shot up more than one bra size. This is basically the state where I am today, with my puberty having more or less completed after over two decades.

My body is now essentially female, with the addition of a penis and a closed-off vagina. During each monthly cycle, I suffer the usual pains on one side of the abdomen and some cramping and pain in the perineum, as has apparently been the norm since I was 11 years old.

What I have found is that despite the help I did receive in Germany, there is no use in me trying to find medical help, including diagnostics and reconstructive surgery, after spending fifteen years searching for it. I have found no support networks for intersex people and no intersex organisations, even when some claim to be.

In the Netherlands, the gender teams prefer to use the non-medical term 'Disorders of Sex Development' (DSD) instead of 'intersex', which would imply a severe medical defect instead of the benign medical condition that most intersex conditions are. In Germany, the DSD term is also used, along with the more general 'rare disease', as I noticed again with a recent attempt at a German hospital.

Although at this point I have learned a lot about my body and I am no longer bound to hormone therapy, the past years have been hugely traumatic to me. Nobody should suffer this kind of treatment at the hands of so-called medical professionals and psychologists. Gender teams should not force intersex people to believe that they are actually transsexual. Doctors should also not operate on intersex infants to erase the ambiguous genitals like they're some horrendous defect.

I was lucky that my vagina was not open at birth, or I would likely have grown up wondering about an odd scar on my abdomen like so many others. Yet despite all the positive things that have happened over the years, to know that I can never trust doctors and psychologists again, that society sees us intersex people more as curiosities and freaks than as functional human beings…all of that is very tough to accept.

I once imagined that I could have had reconstructive surgery to have the vagina reconnected to the perineum and labia constructed out of the now useless remnants of the scrotum so that I could live the rest of my life as a healthy hermaphroditic human. That now seems like a foolish dream, and I instead have to accept that every month fluids are draining into my abdomen for later re-absorption, as if my abdomen is some kind of sanitary pad.

Never getting those last answers about my body, having my body referred to as a medical disorder, and accepting that I'm not worthy of medical help – those are the toughest things about growing up like this. Although my mother and a number of other people along the way accepted me without question and helped me in any way they could, ultimately the medical system refused to yield.

I am still trying to change this somehow. Not just for myself, but for others like me. To finally make the world see that we, too, are human beings. That our bodies aren't shameful or 'wrong'. That no matter what our bodies look like or how we feel, it is simply what and who we are. The overly simplified representation in the books we were given to read as children of humans being one of a binary doesn't do anyone a service.

All our bodies are unique, because DNA and hormones aren't binary. The only thing that is binary are societal gender roles, which is the thing that seems to have had the biggest impact on my puberty. Regressive values and views seem to have led to the reality of my body being pushed away, to be replaced with a more convenient reality for society.

I began to write my autobiography a number of years ago after having been contacted by a publisher. Now that things have quieted down somewhat for me, I hope to have it soon finished and published. My wish is that it will allow others to read about my experiences and make up their own mind about what it means to them and to society as a whole.

Navigating puberty is tough enough without the added

complication of working out what it means to be intersex without the right help.

What next?

- **My personal blog** (*mayaposch.blogspot.com*) – which details many of the experiences in this essay in (much) more detail
- **My personal site** (*mayaposch.com*) – which also has sections about the intersex experience:
    - *mayaposch.com/literature_intersex.php*
    - *mayaposch.com/intersex_issue.php*
    - *mayaposch.com/media.php*
- **Gender Mosaic: Beyond the Myth of the Male and Female Brain** by Daphna Joel and Luba Vikhanski

blood and bone

osteoporosis at 23

by Georgia Priestley

As a child I was always the most active. I would ride my bike around the street for hours, cutting corners and pretending that I was defending the Yellow Jersey. I would never wait for my food to go down before running and playing with my friends – then get the inevitable stitch – then start again as soon as I could. I would practice holding my breath under water until I could easily swim the width of the pool. I would always climb the highest tree; rollerblade the fastest; reach the mountaintop first. I loved the feeling of cold air ripping through my lungs, and my heart pounding in my chest, and the exhilarating thrill to feel each muscle contracting and working to push my body forward. My only competitor was myself, and I beat her every time.

When adolescence came, I found that I was no longer in competition with myself, but with every other girl in school.

Suddenly it didn't matter how fast I could run or how long I could hold my breath – all that mattered was what I looked like and how I spoke. It was very important to have straight hair – and an extreme side fringe of course – and even more important to have the correct school bag. Bright rucksack or faux leather handbag? Jane Norman or Hollister? These were all crucial questions. Who can be the girl to look the most like all the other girls, yet frame it as effortless individuality? Who can have the shortest skirt (yet not be a 'slut') and the blondest hair (but not be 'fake') and the most expensive phone (but not be a 'posh bitch')? Who can be the prettiest and the skinniest? Any difference was preyed upon as a weakness, and any weakness meant that you would be eating lunch a la solo, bitch.

As we continued to grow, we continued to compare ourselves, and as our access to the wider world grew via the internet and the media, we began to compare ourselves to the women we found there too. I distinctly remember watching an episode of the teen drama *90210* and realising that these perfect 'teenage' girls, with their perfect boyfriends and perfect lives, looked nothing like me. They were all size zero with not an ounce of fat on them, apart from their perfect super-model breasts. I had already begun to notice that I was filling out compared to my friends. Given my height, I was a perfectly healthy size, yet I felt awkward and blob-ish. My stomach was slightly round, and I could grab at fat around my hips. I saw the boys in *90210* running their hands over the washboard abs of the girls, holding on to their tiny waists.

When I ran my hand over my own stomach it felt wrong. If being skinny was to be worshipped, where did that leave me?

I decided to become the skinniest I could be. Initially it worked. The girls at school would tell me how lucky I was to have my body and would ask for advice on how to get such a flat stomach. My boyfriend would squeeze my tiny waist with a smile and tell me I looked great. I felt amazing. Sometimes the feeling of starvation would make me feel delirious, almost like a natural high. And the better I felt and the more compliments I got, the more I would push myself to extremes. I started working out more too. I would go on long runs over the countryside near my house, basking in the golden glow of the setting sun, and admiring the slim silhouette of my shadow running on the grass beside me. By the time I was 18 even my friends, who had once admired my body, were getting concerned. I was deaf to comments that I was too skinny and would angrily deny that I had an issue with food.

All this time I had been on the contraceptive pill. My period had started quite late, when I was age 15, and I went on the Pill pretty much straight after this. When I came off the Pill age 17, my periods stopped. This was not of great concern to me. Having lived the majority of my life without periods, their absence was not missed, nor did it worry me. It was only after pressure from my mother that I went to the doctor about it.

The doctor told me that my lack of periods, known as 'amenorrhea', was down to my low bodyweight. She told me if I was to get my period back, I would need to get up to a healthy weight. She explained how when women lose weight to an excessive level their body goes into survival mode and this affects hormone levels. The starved body believes that the environment does not have the resources to support a child, so the menstrual cycle is stopped through the suppression of oestrogen and progesterone. She touched on the fact that menstrual issues may make me more likely to develop weak bones, or diseases like osteoporosis, in the future. I imagined my older self. She seemed very far away.

I went to university and consented to my body's demand to put on weight. By this time the body ideal imposed on me by society had changed anyway – now I had to be fit with a big booty. I delved into a world of YouTube gym tutorials and home workouts. I became obsessed with macro nutrients and squats and deadlifts and #girlswholift. I gained muscle quickly and felt strong. I was squatting with half my body weight and deadlifting twice as much. Again, I was competing with myself, and it felt good.

When I was 20, I had my first serious injury. I was squatting 25kg and felt a big twinge in my lower back. The next year of my life was plagued by intense back pain, caused by sitting for too long, or standing for too long, or walking for too long. I had to stop exercising, apart from gentle Pilates and swimming. Chronic back pain affected my social life, my sex life, and my self-confidence.

Having suffered chronic pain, I began to realise how remarkable the functioning body is. How we take for granted the subtle movement of each individual muscle, tendon, and bone, working smoothly and effectively as one holistic unit. To experience an entire day without suffering pain became a miracle. I saw people around me running and walking, even slouching on a sofa, with ease, and without realising the gift they had in doing so. As I healed, I began to love my own body for its functionality. It slowly dawned on me that the body ideals fed to me throughout my life were a lie. The ideal body is one that works, and one that is loved.

Over the next few years I managed to reach a healthy, albeit slightly low, BMI. I looked healthy and felt good. I still exercised, but in moderation, and stuck to activities like cycling and circuits. I stopped looking in the mirror constantly and began to repair my relationship with food. Still my period did not return.

At the start of 2017, age 23, I got injured again. I was cycling and suddenly felt a sharp pain in my coccyx at the base of my spine. I am still unsure what the injury was exactly, but I was unable to sit down for around five months without being in severe pain. My doctor was concerned to hear that I had injured myself doing a very low-impact activity such as cycling. She was more concerned to hear that I had not had a period for around seven years. Although it is against NHS guidelines to refer young patients for an osteoporosis scan, known as a DEXA scan, she suggested that we investigate the density of my bones to check that everything was in order. Neither of us expected the results that followed.

On 7 March 2017, I was diagnosed with severe osteoporosis, at the level you might expect in a woman over the age of 80. I was confused, shocked, and completely distraught. How could this happen to me when I was only 23? What did this mean for the future? I tried to search online for help, but all advice was (and still is) targeted at women over the age of 60. I read that those who suffer osteoporosis are likely to break their hip and suffer an early death. I read that there was no cure.

Hormonal health and bone health are intrinsically linked, specifically oestrogen and bone growth. This means that women are much more likely to get osteoporosis than men and, as oestrogen levels decline during the menopause, the chances of osteoporosis increase. Oestrogen is vital to bone growth as it supports osteoblasts – the cells that produce bone. Without oestrogen, osteoblasts are not sufficiently supported, and bone-absorbing cells called osteoclasts overpower them. This leads to the gradual loss of bone, as the body then has more cells which absorb bone than cells which produce bone.[1]

Osteoporosis, which literally means 'porous bones', is diagnosed when the bone becomes more than 25% less dense than the average (mean) bone density for that particular age group. There is also osteopenia, the 'precursor' to osteoporosis, where bone density is 15%–25% less dense than the mean bone density for that particular age group. When you have a DEXA scan, which measures bone density, you are given scores for your lumbar spine, hip, and femur, which relate to your bone density in comparison with what would be expected at your age.[2]

At age 23, my scores were as follows:

- 7% less bone density than the average 23-year-old in my hip
- 16% less bone density than the average 23-year-old in my femur
- 34% less bone density than the average 23-year-old in my spine

Suddenly, the back injuries made sense. I had been trying to live my life like any other 23-year-old, when I had the spine of somebody over the age of 80.

It was clear that my restricted eating had fundamentally damaged my hormonal health, which in turn had been sucking the density out of my bones for years. I should also mention that I had been on a 'flexitarian' diet during the year prior to my diagnosis, eating primarily plant-based foods and avoiding dairy and beef, to reduce my carbon footprint. I thought I had been eating healthy and I thought I *was* healthy, especially as my BMI had been classed as at a healthy level for the past couple of years. Yet my bones had been silently suffering and slowly deteriorating.

It was time for another revolution in my attitude to food and to my body. I was going to have to try to get my period back as soon as possible by putting on weight and reviving my hormones from the grave. I was to eat a balanced and nutritious diet, ensuring healthy fats such as those from meat, fish and dairy were a staple to each plate. Spurred on by fear,

I gained nearly a fifth of my body weight in four months. I also began to take supplements – calcium, vitamin d, vitamin k2, and magnesium – a selection partly recommended by my doctor, and partly informed by my own research.

Five months after my diagnosis the first spots of blood appeared in my knickers. I cried. I was overwhelmed with happiness, and a pure, distilled relief that my body had finally received what it needed to function as it should. My first period was a visual symbol of triumph over my issue with food.

Over the next few years I enjoyed my introduction to the monthly cycle and the highs and lows that come with it; the middle days when I practically emit a glowing, positive energy and feel arousal until it aches; the latter days when I feel an agitated discomfort and unprompted anger at the world, until the blood and cramps come, followed by a tiredness accompanied by melancholy, before the process starts all over again. Even when it sucks, it is still a beautiful novelty to me.

In June 2019, I had my second DEXA scan. My oestrogen and progesterone had been at a normal level since my periods started. I had been eating a healthy and varied diet and had managed to maintain my bodyweight.

My results were as follows:

- Increase in bone density from −7% to −4% in hip
- Increase in bone density from −16% to −14% in femur
- Increase in bone density from −34% to −29% in lumbar spine

Bone growth is a long and sometimes irregular process, so to have these improvements in little over a year was, to quote my doctor, 'remarkable'. My results are a testament to the importance of regular periods for bone health, and the vital importance that diet has in supporting our hormones.

Today, I am 25, and I still have osteoporosis. I hope that my bone density will continue to improve. Perhaps one day my bone density will be classed as 'normal' – what a remarkable word.

Sometimes I will have a bad week and compare myself to the women around me. Before I am aware, my clothes feel a little looser, and I become conscious of negative thoughts again. It takes effort to turn the mind away from the 'body-ideal' propaganda that is force fed to us at every turn. It takes a force of will to remember that a body is made to be functional and is not just an aesthetic product, when everything around us tells us otherwise. I will strive to love myself regardless. I will no longer be defined by the expectations of society.

Currently, my level of activity is still restricted due to the likelihood of fracture. I am told to do 'weight bearing' activities, which produce stress on the bone to promote growth, but not enough to cause injury. I try to never forget how lucky I am in my ability to move; to walk down the river Thames to town on a sunny day, or dance with my friends on a night out, or stand at a gig for hours swaying in the crowd. I hope to run again one day – as carefree as I did as a child – but I am content.

I am writing my story in the hope that more people become aware of premenopausal osteoporosis and osteoporosis in general. My story is quite unique, and of course not every person with osteoporosis has shared my experience. However, I think that most people have little or no idea of the vital role that hormones play in bone health and are largely unaware of osteoporosis as a common disease. It is becoming more prevalent, with 50% of women over the age of 50 experiencing a fracture caused by osteoporosis.[3]

I also think that, like me, many young women develop issues with food during their late teens and aspire to be unhealthily skinny. I was concerned to hear my friend tell me that they had overheard some teenage girls celebrating the fact that their periods had stopped, as this was a sign that they had reached their ideal body weight. Young women need to be informed of the importance of periods in maintaining bone health, with emphasis on the fact that changes can occur *right now*. And the media has so much to answer for, with its cultivation of an unobtainable physical aesthetic, and the promotion of a culture of comparison. Fundamentally, we should encourage each other to promote a mindset of self-love and acceptance. We should admire the body for what it is, rather than punish it for what it is not.

What next?

- **Beat Eating Disorders** (*beateatingdisorders.org.uk*) – Beat is a support organisation for individuals with eating disorders. It provides a free, non-judgmental peer support hotline.

what a difference a day makes

how my middle-aged zest for sex was a catalyst for change

by Lins Ringer

I WAS 53 years old, sensible and hard-working. A single mother of grown-up kids, through the menopause and out the other side, and I was obsessed with sex.

I didn't have any, but I wanted to. I was hot for it. Sex was on my mind whenever I was not at work; sometimes when I was. I didn't act on it, but I dreamed about it. I hungered for it.

Although I didn't have menopause lessons in school, and my mum didn't sit me down and tell me what would happen, I thought I had a good idea how things would be when the time came. I was just starting my independent life when she became perimenopausal. We were pretty close, so I knew a bit about how she was, though obviously we never talked about (she whispers) *intercourse*.

It all started the first time I arrived at the bus stop with sweat pouring down me. I had to take my coat off as soon as I got on or people would have noticed the pure aura of heat that I was radiating. Up, down, up, down I had been in the night, and consequently so ratty in the morning I could have bitten the head off a saint. I worked with my hands all the time, but the pain caused by the tiniest pressure on my joints said 'Stop!'. I was 45 going on 90.

I went to the doctor and she said, 'No, not yet, not at your age', but I reckoned differently. An early menarche is often an indicator for the Change of Life, and I was ten when my monthlies began. I went back home, looked on the internet and found my complaints staring me in the face, all under the same heading – '*menopause*'. I noticed that number four on that NHS *Common List of Symptoms* is 'Reduced sex drive (libido)' and I remember thinking that I wasn't looking forward to that. Little did I know.[1]

Men and women of all ages write about the menopause and there are common themes: physical symptoms like dryness, loss of sensation and sensitivity in the genitals and nipples; mood swings – by which they mean running the gamut of emotions like anger and sadness, which are more extreme than usual; and sexual changes – mostly focusing on women not wanting penetration or finding it uncomfortable. Although you can find the occasional reference to changes in sexual desire during pregnancy, you won't find much about being ripe for it in your middle-aged years. The spikes in oestrogen which cause the pre-menopausal stage often result in bodily sensations which surprise and shock you into sitting up and taking note.

Nine years after that visit to the doctor and my periods had been erratic: 40 days with nothing, then one hot on the tail of the other; scarcity followed by flooding; a regular 28-day cycle as it had always been, and then, at last, none. A quick flick through a medical encyclopaedia will reveal this isn't unusual. This pattern is normal. Finally, I was back where I started: no bleeding, hormones settled down.

Except not.

My hormones and I have always had a love-hate relationship. First it was the pain which brought me home from school every month and to hospital a couple of times in my twenties. Then I got pregnant when I tried not to be and had an abortion. My first child was planned – beautiful, no problem – but miscarriage after miscarriage meant that the second child only came after a great deal of heartache and tenacity. Immediately after her birth, while I was still breastfeeding, I was pregnant again – termination number two. Despite an early, hidden proclivity to lesbianism, I was raised to be in an ongoing heterosexual relationship if I wanted children, and it wasn't until the marriage ended that I came out.

I had never gone in for identifying as a woman particularly. A feminist, yes, but being a woman seemed to be a mixed blessing, if my upbringing and the general status of women in the twenty-first century was anything to go by. According to the medical profession (and everyone else who takes their word as gospel), puberty and the onset of bleeding is the start of 'womanhood'. Presumably, then, the Change of Life is the start of *not* being a woman. 'Woman' in the Collins dictionary equates to 'female', that is, someone who produces gametes/ova/eggs and can therefore bear children. This adds another dimension. If a woman is a female and a female is about being reproductive, then describing a woman as someone who bleeds every four weeks is a reductive term, the corollary of which is that if you don't, then you are not.

So, those of us who are post-menopausal aren't women. My sisters whose monthly bleeds have stopped due to stress, eating difficulties, and myriad other reasons, whatever the age, wouldn't be women either. Nor would those who have had a hysterectomy or who are undergoing hormone treatment for breast or uterine cancer. People who were born without a uterus would definitely not be, according to this outdated way of thinking, whether they self-identified or not. Although Simone de Beauvoir famously said that a woman is not born, but becomes, others have controversially stated that you can't be a woman if you weren't born one, whatever operations you have (Germaine Greer, Jenni Murray).

Having daughters in their early twenties, right at the other end of the hormonal scale from me, also served as a stark reminder of where I had been, and of what I now wasn't. They and I were each born with two to seven million primordial follicles, depending which source you consult. These pre-eggs formed while we were being cosseted warmly and wetly in a womb, unsuspecting. Biologically born to be reproductive vessels, it was the hormones doing their own thing which made us like that. Despite 350,000 falling by the wayside, metaphorically speaking, by the time we reached child-bearing age, we still had 400,000 to do what we wanted with.[2] According to the textbooks, by the time I hit this horny stage, my eggs had all died. But what if they hadn't? If there were some left and my hormones were still being activated, would that explain what was happening to me, seemingly against my will?

It seems to be a little-known fact that a body can make a last-ditch attempt to reproduce, even when anyone in their right mind would think it was far, far too late. Over time I pieced it together. Bit by rather painful and ashamed bit, I was able to look at myself objectively (having time to walk and be alone is great for that) and begin to work out what had just happened. It was what R Morgan described as, 'The subtle approach of menopause, distant and then nearer echoes but echoes which conversely precede the sound'.[3]

Part of coming out after my marriage ended was the happy realisation that I would never again have to face a penis in the face, so you can imagine my horror when I found myself, years later, fantasising about penetrative sex. It was after I ceased bleeding altogether that I went from being a functional, feminist lesbian to being someone who sat extensively on the sofa watching heterosexual and predictable rom coms and imagining being the 'girl in the film who gets the guy'. What it felt like in my tactile, imaginative, emotive and spiritual self was that I was fertile, nubile and desirable. Back came the Georgette Heyer/Jilly Cooper-reading, romantic slow-dancing me of my teen years that I thought I had bid farewell to. More than that: what crept up on me and took me totally unawares was the lust, the sheer lust which started to take over my waking and sleeping mind. There were times when I only just managed to stop myself from going out to stand on a street corner with my fishnets on. It was only because I was brought up properly – no, because I was scared – that I stayed at home. Alone. The 'wild, hormone-fuelled pursuit of penetrative sex' of one's twenties that S Manguso describes, was unexpectedly back with a vengeance.[4]

There I was questioning my sexuality like a twentysomething, and privately longing for union with – I still couldn't believe it – men. And what was it like? First, I started to think about sex more often. I could feel it between my legs (where else?), a full-on preparatory moistness *down below* (as my mother brought me up to call it), an urge which had nowhere to go. It was like being halfway to orgasm a lot of the time – tingling in my legs, a sort of fizziness in all my limbs. There were raunchy images, dreams which took up my waking and supposed-to-be sleeping self. When I was growing up it was made clear that this sort of activity was the prerogative of cis males.

In between these busy fantasies, it became clear that I was not where I wanted to be, not enthused by life, so perhaps it was no wonder I 'left' it periodically and flew away to imaginary love islands. I was spending more time with my mother, who was in her late seventies and nursing her second husband.

They married when each was halfway through their eighth decade, giving me hope for my own future. One morning she was telling me about their oh-so-romantic courtship, and perhaps a little of the fairy dust brushed off onto me, because that afternoon I had an unexpected, real-life encounter with an old flame. The pleasure derived from smooching left me as sure as I had ever been: no way was I going to live through another 50 years (the women in my family live to a ripe old age, my great-aunt died at 107) without such joy! Off I went to Spain, alone, walked the Camino, had a passionate affair, and the rest is herstory.

Although it doesn't seem as if this sort of crazy sex drive is written about, it is acknowledged that women can find themselves with some redefining to do in mid-life: kids left home, ongoing job, perhaps a complacent marriage. What I then did, by following my instincts and the mad hormones responsible for sexual desire, was all double-dutch to me.

With its emphasis on being good, following our leaders, not saying 'boo' or rocking the boat, life in the Northern hemisphere for many women at menopause is restrictive. The term cronehood hardly sounds enticing when you still feel able to be up-and-at-it. This story is a micro-version of a macro-situation – hormones prompt women to push past boundaries, to reach out for new adventures, resulting in a new sense of self-definition. The cycles, no, for some, the tidal waves of a female life, from birth through puberty and menopause are nothing except movement, pure and simple. Movement takes us somewhere, motivates, whereas too much staying put makes for stagnation, and that includes thoughts and feelings. Hormones are arbiters of change, molecular kicks up the fanny.

I seriously upset the aforementioned daughters, and others. It turns out that being at different times of our lives means we not only have different requirements (they are ready to settle down and have babies, to be monogamous; I was looking for satisfying commixing), but our previously fixed ethics can adjust too. You could say I returned to the sixties of my childhood, as a fully-fledged woman, and made the most of it when I could. My advice is not to share this kind of thing with the young. Stick, instead, to women your own age who might have an inkling that they, too, need a shake-up.

Let's face it, what I went and did is not something we are encouraged to do (except by each other after a lot of wine, maybe). Using the female sex drive as a pointer to rearrange your life at this age is not seen as responsible or advisable – blimey, it's not even entertained – but it was where my body led me. Looking back, I am not sure if I was creatively stymied and just needed a good fuck to move myself on in that department, or whether I simply had to satisfy those mysterious and pesky chemical messengers, those androgynous envoys of the human race whose job it was to dupe unsuspecting 50-year-olds into perpetuating the species, whatever the outcome.

There's nothing like an extreme of something to cause the pendulum to swing back in the other direction, and hormones are no exception. Back and forth they surge, at once flooding us with the drive of oestrogen and testosterone and then receding to progesterone-shrivelled wobbliness. After all that excitement, I was on my way, literally. Walking long-distance slowed me down so I could start to hear the mysterious inner workings of myself. What I was made to believe I should feel and do at my age, was not actually what I wanted. I tried to return to my normal, frantic pace of life, but the stressful yearning returned with a vengeance. One way and another, over a period of three years, I radically challenged many of my own preconceptions about the work-life balance, my womanly and motherly role, accepted I must be bisexual, and before long new avenues opened up.

Oh! I also started to write, and once I did, I couldn't stop satisfying my lust for it!

What next?

- **Menopause Support** (*menopausesupport.co.uk*) – Menopause Support raises awareness within the workplace for all employers to have menopause guidelines in place to be able to support women experiencing symptoms.
- **Make Menopause Matter change.org petition** (*www.change.org/p/penny-mordaunt-mp-make-menopause-matter-in-healthcare-the-workplace-and-education-makemenopausematter*)
- **Menopause Exchange Blog** (*menopause-exchange.co.uk/blog*)

a period piece

on pcos, pmdd,
and the nhs in 2020

by Jo Ross-Barrett

I STARTED MY period in Year 6, around the age of ten. By this point, we'd had classes about reproduction, but they mainly focused on frogs and rabbits so there were a lot of questions around how that information applied to humans. My mum had once given me a talk that I barely remembered by the time my period started, something about how 'ladies' bleed 'once a month'. It was uninformative and unmemorable – I only know about it now because I later confronted her about why she hadn't taught me about this, and she claimed she did. We had no education on menstruation until I was in Year 8, aged 12 to 13.

So at the beginning, my only source of information was other ten-year-olds whispering amongst themselves at lunchtimes, occasionally asking 'Have you *started* yet?' as an interrogation out of the blue. I did not want to admit that I had. I decided I would admit it when I hit 12, as books never seemed to mention it before that sort of age. Bear in mind that my house did not have a computer with internet access at this point, and we primary school kids weren't allowed to use school computers without supervision. Smartphones were a long way off. The *only* source of information I had access to without (as I then saw it) undergoing public humiliation was listening to those girls.

None of them talked about the gradually worsening achiness I felt in my chest that warned me about what was coming a day or two ahead. None of them talked about the pain that forced me to down paracetamol at every minimum interval just to make it manageable. None of them talked about the misery that overwhelmed me for two weeks out of every four. None of them talked about 'PMS' or 'PMT' except as a joke. None of them talked about stuffing their underwear with tissue paper to avoid stains or pad shopping so they could maintain plausible deniability. Their main concerns were whether it was possible to have a bath or go swimming while you were on your period. So I kept quiet, feeling ashamed and miserable.

While I didn't know the term non-binary then, I had known throughout primary school how much I wanted to distance myself from conventional femininity – and this seemed like just another way I was being forced into a role I never wanted to play. Even my own body conspired against me, remoulding my chest into curves I never asked for, regularly putting me through pain and misery, and thereby reminding me that many people would only ever see me as a sex object and/or baby-making machine. Had I ever been told about puberty blockers, and been educated about puberty before it hit me, I would have *begged* for them. But I didn't learn about them until I was at university, and by then a lot of damage had already been done.

I was a straight-A student. I worked hard, loved studying, and – as a then-undiagnosed autistic kid with underdeveloped social skills – was disliked by many of my peers. Maybe it would have been easier to make friends if I hadn't been assailed by hormones that made me easily irritable and sad half the time, and if I hadn't been forced to work as normal while hiding the fact I was in agony almost a quarter of the time. Maybe if we'd had proper education about our bodies and menstrual cycle when it was relevant, instead of up to four years late, I would have felt more comfortable seeking support and advice from my peers or the adults in my life.

But as it was, one of the clearest memories I have from high school was when my Cooking teacher – who was a young, sympathetic, presumably cis woman – noticed my face had drained of colour and I was in very real pain, and told me to just sit still and rest for her lesson. She was the only teacher who ever gave me any accommodation for my period the whole time I was in school, and this was the only time it ever happened. Two hours of sitting blissfully still, not being expected to act like nothing was wrong. Two hours where I could catch my breath, try to ride out the waves of pain, and not feel pressure to force myself to work in order to avoid being yelled at or having my grades slip. Aged 16, I got almost straight As at GCSE. My cis male cousin got mostly A*s – the next grade up, which is worth more points for future university applications. Granted, he had the privilege of going to a private school while I was at a failing one that was later shut down, but I am certain that if my body hadn't been sabotaging me, I would have got similar or better results.

Years later, while visiting home from university, my best friend's little sister asked me why I had a moustache. The older girls in the room chided her for being rude, but I didn't mind. I'd never really paid attention to my lips before, except when one got a slight scar, but she was right – the hairs there were slightly darker than on the rest of my face. I felt a little embarrassed and self-conscious – after all, the beauty norms I'd been exposed to all my life had never touched upon this, so it must be a problem, right? I decided to ask my GP the next time I was there – and that was how I learnt about Polycystic Ovary Syndrome (PCOS) and finally got a diagnosis after a blood test confirmed my high androgen count. My lifelong sensitivity to sugar, above-average BMI and agonisingly bad periods and PMDD suddenly all made sense. I was also informed that PCOS can lead to infertility. I had been terrified of pregnancy since I was about four years old and first gained a concept of it as something that could happen to me some day, so the prospect of potential infertility was far less upsetting for me than it would be for many people. Around the age of ten, with a little help from the Tracy Beaker stories, I realised that there were lots of young people in need of foster carers, and if I wanted to help raise someone, I could support a young person who already existed and needed. When I learnt about abortion in science class in high school, I was so relieved to know that if I somehow ended up pregnant, there was a way to end it. But the prospect of potential infertility – and of never having to fear getting pregnant in the first place – was a massive relief for me.

Since I am AFAB (assigned female at birth), my GP readily offered me oestrogen-based hormones as a way of 'easing the symptoms' of PCOS a bit. It makes sense that the Pill in its various forms is so readily available, given its popularity as contraception, but I can't help but wonder how many years it would have taken for me to get hormone treatment if I'd said no and asked to try testosterone to combat my periods instead.

While the first variant of the Pill I tried wasn't right for me, Gedarel has been much better at suppressing my periods so I don't have to go through one every month. Instead, I take it for around three months non-stop, until my chest begins to ache and my mind goes back to its PMDD misery. Sometimes I only realise my period is probably due because of intrusive thoughts about suicide (and no, I am not in any danger from them, thank you for your concern but it's as fine as it can be). Breakthrough bleeds, which are basically mini-periods, have to happen eventually because there's only so much womb lining your body can handle. Continuing to take Gedarel during a breakthrough bleed just makes it last longer, so I usually stop taking Gedarel once those warning signs happen.

I wish I could say that having my period is easier now, but it isn't – just less frequent, though that in itself is a blessing.

With all that in mind, you can probably understand why I am deeply interested in the possibility of getting a hysterectomy – no womb would mean no more period agony or fear of unwanted pregnancies – and possibly an oophorectomy (because perhaps no ovaries would mean less hellish hormones making me miserable and pushing thoughts of self-harm and suicide into my mind). My GP certainly understood, and referred me to the Reproduction and Endocrinology department of a hospital for specialist advice.

However, when I finally had an appointment, I did not receive that advice. Instead, I received condescending comments about being 'too young' to make this decision (aged 24), because I 'might change my mind'. This person went on to insist I should try the Merina coil (despite the fact it would not be suitable for me for various reasons) rather than informing me about the potential risks and benefits of a hysterectomy, which was the whole reason for the appointment. This continued after I informed the consultant that I was an asexual non-binary person who had a lifelong phobia of pregnancy, with full carefully-considered intentions to abort any unwanted pregnancies I might get, and long-held intentions of fostering or adopting if I ever did wish to raise a young person. I firmly believe that in this instance, my experience of NHS care was worsened by cisheteronormativity, lack of understanding about non-binary gender and asexuality, ageism and sexism.

Shortly afterwards, in September 2018, I reached out to a local LGBTQIA+ centre who were having a discussion with a Gender Identity Clinic (GIC) worker on healthcare options. Over email, I explained what had happened and asked for advice. Getting responses was slow, but they suggested I ask to be put onto a GIC waiting list, as the people there would likely be better informed, less biased, and more willing to take me seriously. So in December 2018 I returned to my GP, frustrated and disillusioned, and asked to be put on the list.

As I work on this, it is May 2020. I am still on the waiting list for the GIC and the only contact I had from them was one letter after my referral, saying their waiting lists were so long I would definitely not be seen for at least 12 months. Now almost all GIC healthcare has been postponed as 'non-essential' during the COVID-19 outbreak. I do not know how many years I will have to wait, but I do know that if that first doctor had just taken me seriously and answered my questions, I could have been on a hysterectomy waiting list all this time instead. Her ignorance, biases and perhaps even bigotry were unacceptable, and have had a long-term negative impact on my life. If she ever reads this, I hope she is ashamed and makes a serious long-term effort to educate herself and become a real ally, so she doesn't cause someone else to experience this kind of preventable suffering.

You might be wondering – why don't I just use private healthcare? The short answer is, I am poor. The longer answer is, I am poor because I am disabled due to mental illnesses that are exacerbated by my PCOS and PMDD. I have been fighting hard to build a life worth living, fighting to stay physically unharmed when intrusive thoughts about self-harm leap to my mind, and fighting to find meaning through voluntary work because it's damn hard to get paid work once you have a gap in your paid work history. LGBTQIA+ people are at far higher risk of mental health problems and unemployment than the general population; my healthcare (or lack of healthcare) story is just a drop in the ocean.

I wanted to share my story so that people could see the human impact of intersectional feminist failings within the NHS. The NHS needs to offer timely and appropriate person-centred care that focuses on the individual in a holistic manner, rather than trying to fit each person into the norms that the kyriarchy* has prescribed. It needs to train its staff so they recognise their unconscious biases and root them out of their practice for good. It needs to ensure its services are fit for purpose for every potential user, not just cisgender heterosexuals who fit the prototypical narrative of wanting to have biological children someday. It needs funding and expert education so it can do these things. I know recent governments have put a real strain on the NHS, and that is not NHS staff's fault. But the biases and ignorance of that one practitioner *were* her fault, and the fault of the organisations that trained her and didn't correct her assumptions. We need people and

---

* *Kyriarchy is a term that extends the patriarchy to encompass and link to other structures of oppression and privilege, such as ableism, ageism, racism, sizeism, heteronormativity, cisnormativity, amatonormativity, and so on. The word kyriarchy is used to recognise that overlapping, complicated power strata exist. It focuses on intersectionality.*

organisations alike to do better. I know right now COVID-19 is the NHS's top priority, and I have the greatest respect for all their staff and their efforts during this difficult time. But once this is over, I hope the NHS will be able to evolve to better meet *everyone's* needs.

I'll finish with one last plea to the people of the NHS, from policymakers to front-line workers – transgender, non-binary and intersex people need your help. Many of us cannot afford private healthcare, so you are quite literally our only hope. Please do better by us: take us seriously, respect our agency, give us the information we need to make decisions about our own bodies, and don't waste months or years of our lives with ignorance and gatekeeping. We have to deal with so much of that already. Just give us the help we ask for, without judgement or assumptions, and without life-threatening delays.

What next?

- **Vicious Cycle PMDD** (*viciouscyclepmdd.com*) – Vicious Cycle is a patient-led project, passionate about raising awareness of Premenstrual Dysphoric Disorder, and improving the standards of care for those living with the condition.

change

the bitter pill medicine must continue to swallow

by Annabel Sowemimo

MEDICINE IS AN ever-changing field of practice. As a community sexual and reproductive health doctor, I have seen the things that I learnt in medical school become redundant in the space of a few years. Medical research is influenced by a web of external factors: is the disease of clinical importance? It is politically important (i.e., whose health does it affect)? Who stands to benefit from new research being developed? These are some of the most important factors in generating new knowledge. Medicine has historically (less so more recently[1]) been male dominated, with few Black and brown people in senior positions.[2] Why does this matter? Because research agendas are not solely driven by need but by our own implicit biases, and often seek to meet the needs of those deemed 'normal'.

By default, conditions that affect under-represented groups have a history of being neglected – for example, the slow progress in sickle-cell disease research, a condition which mostly affects those of African descent, or the struggle for effective antiretroviral drugs for HIV, which predominately affects Black and queer communities. Male, white and cis-gendered bodies have been presented as dominant, the archetype, and everything else as inferior.[3] With this in mind it is unsurprising that an area of medicine – sexual and reproductive health – which mostly caters to marginalised groups suffers from a dearth of academic research and investment. The history of reproductive health research unmasks unending horrors, including the legacy of J. Marion Sims, 'the forefather of gynaecology', who fine-tuned several of his surgical procedures on enslaved African American women, and the rife practice of clitoridectomies until the 20th century as a supposed cure of mental illness, 'hysteria' and epilepsy.

Today, many activists (including myself) rally to eradicate the practice of Female Genital Cutting (FGC) thought to affect at least 200 million women and girls,[4] most prevalent in sub-Saharan Africa but also practiced to varying degrees in the Middle East and Asia. Yet, Western medicine has experienced its own fraught history with the clitoris, with doctors performing clitoridectomies up until the late 19th century in Britain[5] and the 20th century in the United States.[6] At the heart of this practice lies the historical disdain that medicine once openly exhibited for those with vaginas.

Clitoridectomy was seen as a solution for those deemed deviant in their behaviour – the most common including enjoying sex too much or being 'hypersexual', undertaking masturbation or being queer.

Large clitorises and longer labia were seen as traits most often possessed by Black women or women of colour, predisposing them to hypersexuality. This is epitomised by the story of Sarah Baartman (also known as Hottentot Venus),[7] a Black African woman of the Khoikhoi tribe (at the time considered by some Western colonisers as the missing link between mankind and apes) who was exhibited across Europe during the nineteenth century as an 'exhibit' – spectators regularly commentating on her large buttocks, dropping breasts or 'elongated' labia majora. After her death, French scientist Georges Curvier dissected her body, including her genitalia, which were stored for public display at the Museum of Man in Paris for half a century. The story of Saarh Baartman reflects the brutal relationship that science and medicine had with women's bodies and in particular colonised ones. Despite the eagerness of nineteenth century medics to remove the clitoris, little research was completed on the organ, with it failing to feature in most medical textbooks until fairly recently. We now know it plays a pivotal role in orgasmic pleasure and likely a smaller role in reproduction yet, the lack of research (despite the clitoris being the subject of much clinical intervention) persists.[8]

Whilst reproductive health research has undoubtedly become more ethical, it would appear that the field is still struggling to overcome stereotypes and our own biases. It takes an average of seven years to be diagnosed with endometriosis;* those with the condition often describe being gaslit by medical professionals and being told that painful periods are normal. Is it possible that the way menstruation is socially constructed as part of womanhood and something to be endured is delaying diagnosis and treatment? Are those affected by endometriosis not seeking care as they buy into these ideas? There are so many unanswered questions surrounding reproductive conditions like endometriosis, and the knowledge gap only grows when we examine conditions affecting Black and brown folk.

Fibroids,** benign growths of the womb muscle, disproportionately affect those of African descent and there has been very little progress in understanding what causes the condition.[9] This means treatment options are often limited to medications that reduce bleeding, hormonal medications, or removal of the fibroid or the womb. Fibroids are associated with heavy menstrual bleeding and infertility; often it is only when these symptoms are a problem that patients present. Many patients often say they were told they 'just had heavy periods' or 'it couldn't be *that* bad'; only when they are severely anaemic are they then listened to. The truth is, we

---

Endometriosis is a condition that leads to endometrial (womb) tissue growing abnormally outside of the womb, often causing very painful menstrual cycles, bowel symptoms and infertility.

** *Fibroids are non-cancerous growths in the womb composed of muscle and fibrous tissue.*

do not know what 'normal' blood loss during menstruation is. Most medical textbooks state it's about 80ml, half an egg cup or 16 teaspoons of blood. Yet most people I speak to think that this is far too little and more often, we ask how frequently the period pad may need changing. It seems strange that so often, patients are told their periods are 'normal' but we have no reliable understanding of what normal is.

Often within gynaecology we utilise hormonal medications containing oestrogen, progesterone, or occasional testosterone to manage reproductive health conditions, those undergoing gender transition and most commonly as contraception.

'I want my implant removed – the irregular bleeding is too much. I can't take the combined contraceptive pill because it gives me mood swings and I find it hard to remember. The depo injection made me gain weight. I just need contraception without any side effects so, what are my options?'

These words (or similar) have been uttered by millions of patients seeking contraception globally. As a health professional, there is a slight sinking feeling when this occurs because you know that for those who struggle with hormonal side effects of medication, finding a suitable form of contraception can seem an impossible task. Yes, there is the copper intrauterine device which is hormone-free, yet that too can come with heavy menstrual bleeding. When it comes to side effects and hormone medication, the truth is our understanding is lacking. Why some people have weight gain and others experience mood changes, or worse still, irregular bleeding, seems to be a bit of a lottery. We know that some of these medications can be a vital tool in preventing pregnancy, improving menstrual pain and stopping heavy bleeding, but understanding who experiences what hormonal side effects is still an area of uncertainty.

As life expectancy has increased, more people are undergoing the menopause – when periods begin to stop due to a decrease in ovarian function leading to a number of other symptoms like hot flashes, brain fog, mood changes and palpitations. Oestrogen can be given to help manage these symptoms which can wreck unending havoc on an individual's life. Until recently there were concerns about the use of hormone replacement therapy (HRT) to help manage menopausal symptoms, as some studies had suggested it increases the risk of cardiovascular disease. While larger scale studies have shown the risk to be much lower,[10] HRT can have much greater benefits on a person's quality of life including reducing the risk of bone disease, improving libido and improving mood.[11] Despite this, information around menopause is still sparse and it is even worse when it comes to Black women; studies suggest that there are far fewer Black women accessing menopause services and possible scepticism about accessing hormonal therapies.[12] When I have enquired amongst some of my own menopausal relatives, several are reluctant to engage with medical professionals due to years of bad experiences – this unfortunately, is extremely common amongst many Black people.

As medicine progresses and we become more inclusive of those of all identities; we must too be inclusionary in our research to ensure that we can best meet the needs of all communities. Over the last few years, we have seen more trans people take their right to transition and try to live their lives to their fullest capacity. Despite this, there is very little existing research on the reproductive lives of trans people and their experiences of utilising hormones during the transitioning process.[13] Often, transfolk utilise blogs, websites and safe social media spaces to make sense of the effects that hormonal changes are having on their bodies. The overall health outcomes for Black transwomen are particularly bleak – experiencing high rates of HIV, experiencing sexual assault and at worst death. We have an obligation that as society becomes more inclusive, so too should our scientific research so that our medical systems are fit for *all* people.

Whilst the medical systems continue to be challenged and remade, a continued effort is needed not just from scientists and medical professionals but also wider society to demand that reproductive medicine caters to the needs of everyone. Hormones are powerful – they can determine our ability to reproduce, live happy, healthy, and fulfilling lives. There are amazing researchers working to generate new information and provide us with more clarity for our patients. We must acknowledge that some of the science has lagged behind, primarily because of who is affected by poor reproductive health. If we do not admit our profession's past errors and acknowledge our blind spots, then we will never truly see the patients that have consistently missed out.

What next?

- **Decolonise Contraception** *(decolonisingcontraception. com)* – A team of interdisciplinary POC sex educators, doctors, campaigners, journalists, researchers, and many others who challenge you to think differently about sexual and reproductive health.

- **SisterSong** *(www.sistersong.net)* – SisterSong is a Southern based, national membership organisation with the purpose to build an effective network of individuals and organisations to improve institutional policies and systems that impact the reproductive lives of marginalised communities.

if rabbits, why not women?

living in a woman's body shaped and kept together by the inventions of men

by Jeanne Sutton

In September 1960, before a panel consisting of Dr. Guttmacher, Dr. Aqviles Sobrero, and Dr. Tietze, I presented the inserter tube, the coil, and a hysterogram of my wife, who had submitted to the first insertion.

> – Lazar Margulies, MD, The Mount Sinai School of Medicine of the City University of New York, from a paper presented at a Symposium on the IUD, April 17, 1974.[1]

Symptoms / Prometheus steals fire

IN 2011, I rented a studio apartment in a tall depressing brick building on the outskirts of Toronto. I'd argue it was almost not Toronto. Getting to the city centre involved two modes of transport. A 1970s palette of bathroom green and murky brown blighted the room and its cramped tributaries. My bed had no headboard – the immovable frame wasn't designed to kiss the wall – and its mattress was stiff plastic-encased foam. When I remember the bad sleep during the study year abroad programme, I remember I tolerate too much discomfort. Sometimes it's okay to ask to speak to the manager.

Before Toronto, my periods were background noise – cramps, a spectrum of fresh reds and clotty livers. Over the months I existed in Canada, they grew worse. When something happens inside of you every four weeks, a lady clockwork, the something that happens inside of you is your measuring stick.

I collapsed in spring, woke up on my floor, walked to a clinic. A few weeks and inconclusive tests later, a doctor hypothesised it was endometriosis. I returned to Ireland that summer and a consultant examined me. The condition is usually diagnosed with laparoscopy. His secretary booked my surgery for winter.

Diagnosis / Persephone gets used to the underworld

Endometriosis is a chronic inflammatory condition which occurs in an estimated one in ten women. Men and trans men also suffer. Tissue similar to that which normally grows inside the uterus, endometrium, grows outside the womb. This tissue festers on ovaries, fallopian tubes, the bowel, the pelvis, beyond. One theory says the tissue reacts to the same hormonal stimulation as normal endometrium. Your menstrual cycle can dictate a seesaw of pain, fatigue and other issues. What causes endometriosis remains an unanswered question. Research is ongoing. A common symptom is intense period pain. All our pain tastes different. Mine was and is a magnet trapped in my body trying to make its way to the earth's core. It wants me horizontal and burrowing.

Weeks after the diagnostic surgery, a doctor prescribed an oral contraceptive. The Pill acts as a band-aid to treat some symptoms. Sometimes it takes, sometimes it's useless. I did nothing with the script. Two friends had blamed that specific Pill for relationship friction and dark thoughts that swerved near suicide. At the college health centre, I got a prescription for something else.

In 'Women over 35 Who Smoke: A Case Study in Risk Management and Risk Communications, 1960–1989' in the book *Medicating Modern America*, Suzanne White Junod ascribes 'lingering suspicions' about the Pill's safety to its original marketing.[2] Although launched as a contraceptive in 1960, the Pill was first used in 1958 as a hormonal treatment for menstrual irregularities. When the medication assumed its intended role as a family planning tool, societal benefits took messaging precedence.

Junod mentions how in 1961 *The Lancet* covered the first death associated with Enovoid, the original Pill, but Thalidomide was gripping headlines.[3] Smatterings of data emerged linking the Pill with thrombosis. Still, the medical community's consensus remained that the Pill was more effective than alternatives in terms of preventing conception and posed reduced risk to the female body than pregnancy.

That's still true, by the way. You're in less danger when your blood is an impregnable broth than when you're pregnant.

Treatment / Pandora finds a petri dish

In their introduction to *Therapeutic Revolutions: Pharmaceuticals and Social Change in the Twentieth Century*, Jeremy A. Greene, Flurin Condrau and Elizabeth Seigel Watkins invoke 20th-century German historian Reinhart Koselleck.[4] Koselleck interrogated the manipulation of the term *revolution* by those with skin in the game. Industrialists coined the Industrial Revolution. Their glut of inventions disrupted lives and communities. Their revolution decimated leisure time and made children into workers. The scam needed an amorphous instigator. Blame society itself. Vive la wrong sort of révolution. Nothing is neutral. A narrative implies an author.

The Pill came into being alongside the so-called sexual revolution in 1960s America. But heterosexual relations had already been undergoing a sort of power rebalancing. 19th-century family size diminished thanks to rubber proto-condoms and knowledge of the withdrawal method. Women weren't suddenly liberated with the FDA approval of the Pill in 1960. The Pill was born in clandestine conditions. It was an unfashionable area of research in the country which had just split the atom. Jonathan Eig's 2014 book, *The Birth of the Pill*, details how a small galaxy of individual motives collided in post-war America.[5] In 1951, an elderly Margaret Sanger approached renegade scientist Gregory Pincus with her vision for a contraceptive that would change everything.

Watkins essay '*Reconceiving the Pill: From Revolutionary Therapeutic to Lifestyle Drug*' points out that Sanger's idea correlated with the wonder drug era. Penicillin was saving lives usually taken by war.[6] The public trusted science.

Decades before, Sanger had campaigned to legalise the diaphragm. Now, she was a tarnished star with waning influence. Earlier associations with eugenics proponents cast a shadow. Organisations she had established were tuning her out. Pincus was notorious for his work on a rabbit's ovum in the 1930s that sowed the seeds, or eggs, for IVF technology. The media framed his breakthrough as indecent. Harvard, where he conducted the research, wanted nothing to do with him. According to Eig, Pincus was 'deemed too dangerous'. Some suspected anti-Semitism played a part. At the time of the Sanger meeting, he was running the far-from-fancy Worcester Foundation for Experimental Biology in Massachusetts. Many still regarded him as a genius.

When Sanger asked Pincus if he could deliver her the want of her lifetime, he answered with a probably. Back at the lab, his colleague, the Chinese-American scientist Min Chueh Chang mentioned a piece of research about ovulation in rabbits. Injecting the creatures with the hormone progesterone prevented ovulation. If rabbits, why not women? To answer this, they needed resources.

For decades, millionaire Katharine Dexter McCormick had supported research into schizophrenia. Her husband had the condition. He died in 1947. McCormick inherited his fortune and stopped giving a financial fuck. In the early

1950s, Sanger reached out. They knew each other from the suffrage movement. Sanger presented an idea. To paraphrase Vesper Lynd in the movie *Casino Royale*, McCormick became *the money*. G.D. Searle and Company took over when the enterprise headed for the market.

To test the medication, a Catholic from Boston entered the fray: Dr. John Rock. While Pincus and Chang explored hormones' contraceptive ability, Rock had been querying their potential to treat infertility. Malcolm Gladwell's New Yorker essay 'John Rock's Error' delves into how Rock's faith shaped our use of the Pill.[7] Rock was a man of faith for most his life. He attended mass every morning. He worked to improve the lives of his female patients. Then, years later, a monsignor called him a moral rapist. When Rock was a medical student, he had worked in Boston's Irish tenements, treating women overwhelmed by numerous pregnancies. He didn't get involved with the Pill because he liked a challenge. He threw in his lot because he was a good doctor who helped his patients.

Rock's involvement with the Pill was '*shepherding*' – Gladwell's verb, not mine – the medication through its clinical trials. His respectable front got the Pill across the regulatory line and into the minds of prescribing doctors and the bodies of women. His past held no mutant rabbits.

It took decades for the Pill's darker history to face condemnation. Like how poor women of Puerto Rico were the first subjects of its mass trial. American soil meant stricter, and safer, rules. The Pill was immediately lauded, but eventually, a brewing movement came to the boil. A US Senate hearing in 1970 analysed safety concerns. A 1969 Washington Post column accused the FDA of sitting on data indicating fatality rates higher than published.[8] That same year Barbara Seaman published *The Doctors' Case Against the Pill*.[9] During the hearings, female users were compared to unsuspecting guinea pigs. It was decided a patient insert, the first of its kind, be included with the product going forward. Use in America dropped in the 1970s. The level of hormones used in various versions of the Pill also dropped. It's still a popular contraceptive but remains a whispered-about anecdotal bogeyman.

A few months after I finished college in 2012, I got a new doctor. She told me I was on the wrong pill for my issue. I explained my wariness of the initial medicine. She identified another option. I've been on the same second-generation combined oral contraceptive pill – Ovranette – for over seven years.

Side effects / Shaped by Pygmalion

A *Guardian* review of Eig's book called the Pill a 'Promethean gift', referencing Ashley Montagu's observation: 'In its effects I believe that the Pill ranks in importance with the discovery of fire'.[10] He also compared it to nuclear energy. I see the sugary baby planet as the gateway to my own Persephone myth. In that story, Hades kidnaps Persephone to join him in the Underworld. Her mother Demeter, the Greek goddess of fertility, becomes distraught at the loss. As she wanders the earth, plants wilt. Persephone is rescued but must return to her husband for a few months every year. Winter comes whenever she descends. Demeter's sadness returns. Interpretations differ: Hades tricked Persephone into eating the juicy crisp seeds of a cursed pomegranate, or she chose to consume knowing full well the consequences.

The Pill isn't perfect. Asking a medicine which alters the body so much it stops doing its 'duty' to have no side effects is hubris. In return for some control over my body and dimmed symptoms, I've traded a waistline for weight I can't lose. I miss the ease of the concave. My body hair is hedgehog blunt. When I shave above the knee, I expect small insect bite scabs in the regrowth. I keep promising myself laser. Overall, these are small payments.

I feel guilty about my reaction to the Pill when women at parties tell me it momentarily destroyed them. They say it robbed them of themselves. I wonder about the me I don't know. When I obey my pill's schedule, I'm Hades' wife – mistress of one kind of future, both wanting it and there under duress. When I ignore my health needs, I'm the daughter of Demeter, full-on nature. An alternative world lies in the silver of disobedience.

A higher dosage / Eating the pomegranate

For years, I took the Pill the 'normal way'. 21 days followed by seven days' break. That's what the label stuck on the box instructs. The Pill's inventors said so. The break exists because Pincus and Rock thought periods disappearing might frighten women. And they wanted the Catholic Church's approval. Rock portrayed the Pill as 'natural' contraception. It regulated cycles, toned up nature, a souped-up rhythm method.

After all of Rock's philosophical gymnastics and diplomacy, the Church rejected the Pill in 1968 as suitable contraception for its followers. Blame the Pope for stained sheets. We bleed for God.

For me, it was going fine-ish until one break didn't end despite resuming my daily schedule. For weeks my sanitary pad squelched. I was a walking wound. My then-manager said I looked grey. My doctor told me to start taking packages back-to-back, three at a time, then a break. My own bouts of Persephone. That fixed things for a while.

None of this cures endometriosis. The disease is thought incurable. The Pill *manages* the symptoms. In the early days of getting the Pill across the societal line, its secondary effects – how it 'regulated' menstruation and suppressed long bleeds – played a big role. Before designated contraception, it fixed your schedule. Junod noted that in the 1990s, marketing moved from 'life-changing to life-enhancing' – better skin, less bleeding, diminished pelvic pain. A reframed narrative.

Two years ago, my body began to protest again. Nothing rent me entirely undone. I was a creaking ship getting through the storm. My infrequent periods, those planned 'breaks', became chapters of dread. The week began with climbing headaches akin to caffeine withdrawal. Then my bottom half descended into unsexy IBS territory. I placed clothing I liked in small plastic bags and then into bin bags. A former employer commented on my trips to the bathroom. I think she wanted me to apologise, to admit I was disgusting. As she stood in front of my desk, my laptop screen shone up pages about dehydration and warning signs. My GP told me to start taking the Pill continuously, saying something close to, 'You can't live like that'.

The Pill wasn't masking everything anymore. I went back to my consultant. Endometriosis isn't ascertained through ultrasounds. The knife beckons. My consultant had theories about treatment. He would add a hormonal intrauterine device, an IUD, during surgery. It's also a contraceptive. My body can handle and even likes hormones, was the gist. As I left the office, HRT was mentioned. After babies, if I have them, that's my next station of the cross. By the time menopause rolls around, this consultant will be retired. He is, to be weird and honest, my body's sun. Thinking of his loss dizzies me. But I'm not his life's work.

In Greek mythology, Pygmalion was a sculptor who, having denounced women, fell in love with his creation. He wished for a real-life woman identical to his polished work. When he next kissed the statue, its lips were warm. A former slab of rock transformed into the woman he wanted. When you go into a hospital for surgery, a medical team member talks through the operation's potential outcomes and obtains your informed consent. Should your surgeon decide scooping out your ovary is for the best, paper instructs: carve away. You hand them putty. They hand back a new version of you.

The IUD is placed in your womb. Mine is T-shaped, an unfinished crucifix, and contains progestogen. The IUD's history stretches back to a 1909 paper, wherein it is described as two strands of silkworm gut wound together and united by a thin bronze filament placed in the uterus with a metal female bladder catheter.[11] By the 1920s, doctors in Germany were exploring a newer version – Dr. Ernst Gräfenberg's silver ring. At the same time, a doctor in Japan, Dr. Tenei Ota, was forging a similar path. However, Nazis didn't like Jewish doctors, or the idea of preventing an Aryan race. Gräfenberg fled Germany in 1940, finding a position at Mount Sinai in New York. Ota spent the war in hiding after the Axis banned his research.

It wasn't until the 1960s that the IUD came out of the shadows. By then, the Population Council, an organisation founded by a Rockefeller in 1952, wanted to tackle the growing global population. The Council heard various Mount Sinai doctors were using and prototyping IUDs, so it held symposiums, encouraged research, targeted developing countries. In its way, the IUD shared the shady Sanger undertones.

Dr. Lazar Margulies pioneered the modern method of getting an IUD inside a womb. The arms bend down, ready to spring, as it's pushed up through a small tube. Then it blooms inside, adjusting to the t-shape of the uterus at rest. Margulies didn't test the delivery method and device in public clinics. He didn't trust poor women to complain if anything became uncomfortable, unlike his private patients. Well-to-do uterine cavities became the medical research version of the princess and the pea. He sought their unvarnished can-I-speak-to-the-manager feedback.

Like the Pill, the IUD underwent a trust crisis. In a YouTube video dated 1984, a woman with beige hair wearing beige clothes sits in front of a beige curtain. She speaks to camera: 'This important health warning is for women still using the Dalkon Shield, an IUD birth control device obtained in the early to mid-1970s. There is substantial medical opinion that continued use of the Dalkon Shield may pose a serious personal health hazard and it should be removed. If you're still using the Dalkon Shield, its maker A.H. Robins company will pay your doctor or clinic to remove it. It's that important'.[12]

2.5 million women in the US used that IUD. It caused Pelvic Inflammatory Disease and at least 18 deaths. Lawsuits ended A.H. Robins. A design flaw was to blame. The string fibre there to remove the IUD acted as a wick, carrying infection to the womb. Margulies once used the term 'preantiseptic times' when talking about early IUDs. The past is a dangerous country.

The outcome / Some people are Eurydice, others choose to be Orpheus

In *The Makings of a Modern Epidemic: Endometriosis, Gender and Politics*, Kate Seear wrote: 'compliance with medical advice is almost always valorised as a hallmark of responsible citizenship'.[13] I live in a body shaped by the inventions and intentions of male doctors and scientists. It's as if I'm taking part in a paternalistic conspiracy. I'm falling for Hades. I'm

Rapunzel's parents surrendering the future for lettuce. I'm a heavy-on-the-hips sculpture. I'm the princess not objecting to the pea one day, crying about it to a GP the next.

I should be sorry, but I don't regret my collaboration. Profiting from misery and eugenics experiments has saved me. Maybe there is another angle on all of this. When I swallow a pill and tear through a packet without a break, or have penetrative sex with an IUD inside me, I'm telling the Church and the Axis powers to go fuck themselves. I'm a woman chewing tobacco on oilfields I own. I'm not falling down. Is that enough?

What next?

- ***Ask Me About My Uterus*** by Abby Norman
  This is a non-fiction text which switches between Norman's evocative personal memoir as she struggles with endometriosis and accounts of medical history. In the latter sections, she shows how modern medicine has evolved and conspires to doubt female accounts of pain. The Gilda Radner chapter details how the comedian and actress couldn't even leverage her wealth and America's sweetheart status to have her health concerns addressed. In the mid-eighties, she fell ill and for ten months doctors failed to diagnose the ovarian cancer of which she eventually died in 1989.

three magic days

by Alice Tarbuck

THERE COMES A day every month when nothing feels comfortable. When I feel intensely aware of my body, its skin and its edges. When I can smell people acutely, taste things in far too much vividness, when instead of fruit and vegetables, I crave salt and sugar and fat and meat. When I find myself idly daydreaming about blood, or crisps, or both. I find myself wanting to stroke my hands over velvet, wanting to take scented baths, wanting to escape into silk sheets. Every month, I am surprised by it. Shocked that my body makes itself so suddenly and entirely visible to me, as if I settle back down into it after three weeks of near-absence. It is a strange place to come back to: familiar, yes, but not quite my own. I am not on an entirely even keel, here, and things keep happening against my wishes.

On that day, strange though it is, things start to fall into place. On that day, when I'm wearing leggings and a soft wool jumper and can't bear to feel mascara against my eyelashes, I'm also, somehow, suddenly aware of the shape of the universe. It is as if my senses, which are so limited the rest of the time, can strain just beyond their usual endurance point, make out all the shapes and patterns of the visible and invisible. I am able to find the right words. People approach me in bars. I wear revealing clothing with delight, my body suddenly feeling – just for a few days – like something intricate and sexy, to be admired. Almost all of my relationships have started in this strange cluster of days, and many of the job interviews I've had during them have been successful. It is strange to feel that for a brief period, I am able to become, almost, a more successful version of myself. Or indeed – and this is perhaps an even more unsettling thought – I am able to actively access those parts of myself.

The day after that, the tears come. Any lodged injustice, any fear or worry, any heartbreak, any deep-set sorrow that hasn't been resolved in the previous weeks dislodges from where I have been hiding it. It circulates around me, coming back to the throat, choking me, drawing tears. Nothing is too small to affect me, that day. No slight, no sharp-sided memory, no bruise of hurt is permitted to lie still.

Scientists have mapped our emotions to show us where we feel them in the body, and the results indicate that lots of emotions are biologically produced, not simply the product of thought. This 'body atlas' shows us that, for example, anger sits towards the top of the body, but happiness is felt all over the body, and sadness is experienced as an absence of feeling across the body.[1] Our emotions flush and flash across our bodies, involving every part of our systems. One day a month, mine seem to move from their usual colours and textures towards extraordinary vividness: a disco-ball, whirling itself around me. I doubt that's what the Finnish scientists who coined the 'body atlas' had in mind, but that's certainly what it feels like.

Classical medicine, in an alternative model, gave specific emotions particular locations. For example, Aristotle argued that anger was, for certain thinkers, found in 'the raging of blood or heat around the heart'.[2] There was much debate in classical medicine as to the nature of emotions: did they spring up from inside the body, or were they externally located and thus something which was encountered? Views on this varied vastly. For example, among the most widely reproduced views were those of Galen, who believed that 'emotions were occurrences external to the person, imprinting first the soul and then the body'.[3] In contrast to this, Avicenna suggested 'seeing the emotions as part of the virtutes animalis – that is, a natural state of the body'.[4] This might be very basic – surely we have moved past such debates, in all our sophisticated contemporary medical science. But if you think about it, the 'body atlas' is yet another way of attempting to quantify where our emotions come from. One of the aspects of our lived emotional reality which trips us up, I think, is the extent to which emotions seem to appear suddenly, as if out of the murky gloom of our subconscious.

My emotions have always felt located, in the way Aristotle characterises. Fear in the stomach, love across the back, lust like wisps of heat up inside the abdomen. But they are, even more than that, Hippocratic. Although it has of course been entirely disproven by science, I do rather feel that I have four humours, and that when they are out of balance, all manner of things go awry. Awry, askew, adrift – in every sense, when my emotions are off kilter, strange things happen. And every month, my humours become entirely unaligned. It isn't black or yellow bile, it isn't an excess of choler: it's exsanguination.

Hippocrates was interested in menstruation, but mostly as it related to fertility and childbirth, and far less so as a phenomenon in and of itself. Indeed, he characterises menstrual blood as being fast-clotting, like that of a healthy animal sacrifice. This is because, despite blood being a humour, menstrual blood was not seen as having the same effect of disrupting emotional regulation as other kinds of bleeding had. Indeed, menstrual blood barely seemed to belong to the woman, but was indicative of wider important aspects of the running of a household. A 'woman's healthy blood had wider, civic significance; it affirmed that she could replenish the citizen body as well as her own'.[5] The emotional aspect of menstrual cycles – their hormonal component – was not much considered. Nevertheless, I feel precisely this disturbance in humours when my hormones kick in. Anything could happen – the world is out of joint – and there is a delicious opening-up of possibility.

This delicious feeling was with the lived reality of my strange body. For the last ten years, I've been worried about my hormones. Diagnosed with a rare autoimmune disorder at 21, I've spent years having my hormones intermittently monitored. Nobody is sure why a young person ended up diagnosed with a condition that overwhelmingly affects either prepubescent bodies or post-menopausal ones. I was – and remain – a medical mystery, the very least enjoyable sort of marvel. I am one of the people often asked if a medical student can come in to my consultant appointment because I am of interest. I am atypical. I am, with all its dubious associations, *special*. My strange, outlandish hormones and their monthly dances that whirl through my body are, in some way, an excellent compensation for this anxiety. I may not be explicable to science, but for three days a month, sometimes four, I am unbeatable, vigorous, confident, more emphatically present in the world than during the rest of the time.

One of the gifts of being so marked has been an increased and keen awareness of the life and times of my hormones. So much of having an unusual condition means turning amateur detective, and it can be a very helpful way, for some people at least, of coping with trauma. It is far more difficult to feel sorry for yourself when you're donning a metaphorical monocle and sifting through every back issue of the *British Medical Journal*.

I've always been very hormonal, whatever that means. I started menstruating early, and have always experienced the most wide-ranging, life-altering emotional states around the beginning of my period. It feels, often, like being bewitched, out of control of my own body, as if I am taken out of myself, or as if something else is added in.

It is a fascinating feeling, and not one that is very consistently documented. In fact, I know of very few other people who report having these strange enchanted days. Sometimes, I feel more stereotypically premenstrual, angry, irritable and weepy. So weepy. But every second or third month, this glorious technicolour whirl of emotions, confidence and creativity overwhelms me. You are supposed to be miserable before your period – retaining water, experiencing tiredness, spots, a dip in serotonin caused by a low level of oestrogen, and a corresponding dip in testosterone, which can contribute to feelings of low self-esteem. Whatever happens in my body, it does not process these chemical and hormonal changes the same way. Which makes me wonder, of course, what exactly is happening in my body, and how I might both understand it, and use it.

One of the ways I understand my hormonal cycle is by making note of it, marking it – keeping a diary of not just symptoms, but thoughts, too. How do I feel, and when, and what enhances these feelings? I've found that if I act on the first little flutters of creativity, I can get great writing done on these days – but I have to nurture it, act fast, give myself space. I've also found that if I plan dinner parties or dates for around these clusters of days, I go into them feeling happy and excited, and this seems to have a cascading effect, creating even more good feeling. I try to work with the days, rather than ignoring them or dreading the times that they aren't so positive. I create in them – make birthday cards, or start craft projects, because my fierce inner critic is quiet for a little while, and I make the most of it. I burn nice scented candles, I launder my sheets, I have little fits of deep-cleaning. I let my body take me where it wants to, as far as possible – I try to make my body a good place to be in, for those periods of hyper awareness.

Hormones are strange. They are overlooked, often, and they don't behave the way we'd like them to, or in ways that are easily explained. But my hormonal cycle is like a storm tide – it washes up strange blessings on my shore. I am grateful for the way it has carried me through my adult life. Always strange. Always unexpected. But always it takes over my body, and things happen. Hormones are not magic, nor are they Hippocratic. Emotions do not dwell in our bodies; they are caused by our bodies. But, but. Once a month, I throw all of that good logic out of the window, put on ridiculous clothes, cry my heart out, and see what this month has in store. To be in my body is a curious magic, and I am glad of its strangeness. It has served me so well.

What next?

- **The Vulval Pain Society** (*vulvalpainsociety.org*) – The Vulval Pain Society promotes and protects the physical and mental health of sufferers of vulval pain through the provision of support, education, and practical advice.

banana-leaf poultices

black british attitudes to healthcare and medication

by Rianna Walcott

As the COVID-19 pandemic sweeps the world, my grandma tells me with some pride that back in Barbados, where the number of infections still remains in the low double figures and deaths in the single figures, people are returning to the 'old ways'. An island of only 166 square miles with a population of less than 300,000, served by just two main hospitals, she reminds me that quick access to medical care on the island is not always possible or affordable, so in her youth, preventative and holistic medicine was a staple.

Lemon, ginger and honey tea (sometimes spiked with rum) for a cold, poultices wrapped in banana leaves and held firm to the body to draw out infection, a spoonful of foul-smelling cod liver oil or black seed oil a day, and the dreaded bush tea for a 'clear out' if you so much as fart in the vicinity of an elder;

these are the medicines my grandparents brought with them from the Caribbean to the UK, the medicines of my parents' youth and – to a lesser extent – the medicines of mine.

As an advocate for BAME mental health awareness and support, not to mention a user of prescription medication myself, my personal attitudes to mainstream healthcare are quite different to those of my parents and grandparents. I remain aware and critical of the ways in which healthcare systems underprivilege Black people globally and in the UK, through histories of non-consensual medical experimentation on Black people during and after times of slavery,[1] non-consensual sterilisations,[2] disproportionate diagnoses and criminalisation of Black people with severe mental health conditions,[3] and, even now, the disproportionately high mortality rate of Black people infected with COVID-19.[4] Even so, while I still practice the familiar home remedies when I have a cough (that spiked tea is actually very nice, and definitely effective), I'm also perfectly happy to go to my doctor – albeit after applying a little extra pressure to ensure I'm treated fairly.

My mum has fallen somewhere rather different on this spectrum. She is less likely to go to a physician than my grandma or myself, instead believing in diet and exercise as an all-round healer. My mum is diet obsessed, easily captured by fads, and has a strange reluctance towards official healthcare systems. In her mind, most health problems are borne of being fat – with disastrous consequences for me over the course of my lifetime.

As a teenager with severe acne and a brutal period, following my doctor's recommendation I asked for my mum's consent to be put on a birth control pill that promised to regulate both. Instead, I was put on an expensive course of Chinese acupuncture, cupping and foul-tasting teas once a week after school. I've been on every crash diet, cut out every food group there is, tried a myriad of liquids, pills and powders, and have even been banished to a retreat which my sister and I lovingly refer to as 'fat camp': a week long vegetable juice cleanse that we spent in a fatigued stupor, with furry tongues and beetroot coloured stools. We each lost a stone of water weight that we regained with our first meal out of the place.

Now an adult, I am able to take more control of my own health, mentally and physically. I take antidepressants, antibiotics for my acne, and have been on various types of birth control including the contraceptive pill and now an IUD. My mum still objects to me using all of the above because they are cosmetic, mental health related, and related to sexual activity – areas she would rather I treated with diet and exercise, or simply would not think of in connection to me. In a seeming contradiction, my mum has endless respect for doctors and would have been thrilled to see me become one. As my grandparents enter their twilight years, they visit doctors more frequently too.

This conflicting logic had me wondering – what ethnocultural factors make some healthcare issues acceptable and real, and others unacceptable to Black people? How do Black British people balance mainstream healthcare with the holistic? Some research led me to two studies, one by Cooper-Patrick et al. (1997) on Black attitudes towards the use of medication in the treatment of depression, and another by Thorens et al. (2008) on determinants of drug treatment outcomes, such as patients' expectations, attitudes, and adherence to psych medication. I also spoke with several Black British people about their experiences and histories of medication and self-medication.

Family and culture

One of the greatest barriers to accessing healthcare is unsurprisingly family (and wider cultural) opinion. Fears of family disapproval came up repeatedly in interviews, and more specifically a pervasive, cross-cultural suspicion of 'Big Pharma'.

Jamala Abdullahi

My family has very little trust in doctors, because they can never explain what is in the pills they give out. Doctors never ask about how you're caring for yourself, they never look at the bigger picture. My mom especially believes that Western medication brings on more health issues than she already has. Don't get me wrong, we do go to the doctors, but it's more for finding out what the problem is. Then we mostly just find some other way of taking care of it. If it's something serious that we don't have much knowledge on, then we do take the medication while we look for alternative, natural medicines. We're big believers that the body knows how to care for itself, and that if you give it the right ingredients then it works better and acts faster. We also don't want to build dependency on medication, so if we can be without it then we do.

Patients from non-European countries were significantly less often positive about taking medication than patients from the other groups. (Thorens et al., 2008, p. 58)

Dr. Samara Linton

In general, my family don't really like medication. Mum doesn't even like taking painkillers. They think natural and organic is best, and they grew up in Jamaica without access to some of these medications.

Growing up we were able to have ibuprofen and paracetamol when we had bad periods, but on the whole, we never really had much medication. That being said my parents were never against vaccines, and I think that's because they knew that they did good! We always had all of our childhood vaccines and immunisations, and when we moved to the UK we had to get loads more. I was quite sick when I came to the UK – I was always ill with fevers and pains, and they never really knew what was wrong with me, I spent quite a bit of time in hospitals and going to doctors. So, my parents were quite willing to engage from that perspective, but for themselves they never really took much medicine: we have medicines in our cupboard that have been there for years and definitely should have been thrown away.

Mum always has teas – I don't know where she gets them from, bush teas that she'll buy from friends, and herbs that she'll make into teas. She's a big fan of aloe vera, cod liver oil. She'll take vitamins, but natural supplements are always the way she prefers to go. So, I've never had lemsip for a sore throat: it's always been garlic tea. There are fewer side effects, and because it's wisdom that's been passed down through generations, they trust it.

What is your general opinion about taking medications? Non-EU responded 28.6% positive as compared to 68.5% positive from Swiss (read: white) people. (Thorens et al., 2008, p. 59)

I think that the distrust for white colonial systems and medications mean Black people prefer to use alternative, holistic, natural medications. We think they're more 'real', rather than 'chemicals', and that they aren't part of a profit-based system in the same way drug companies may be. I also had bad eczema when I came to the UK but I was never allowed to use steroid creams, it was always some other random cream we bought from the market.

We don't tend to trust healthcare professionals, and often for good reason! Once my sister had this really bad rash, and it wasn't getting better despite all of the things we were using, so my mum took her to the GP. The GP said 'they couldn't see it'. This rash has been harassing my sister, it's bright as day, but she couldn't see it. So, as a result my sister hasn't seen a GP in ages, and even now she thinks it's a waste of time.

It takes so long to get an appointment to then be faced with medical racism, where they can't even see the rash on your Black skin.

Even me becoming a doctor hasn't changed a thing. I ask my parents, why did you send me to medical school if you don't believe a thing I say? They just said 'it's a good job'. It's as though the things I can do are for white people, but not for us. For example, my dad has diabetes now – I've been warning him for years that he was likely to get it because of his lifestyle, his symptoms. Did he listen to me? And now, behold diabetes. They just don't respect Western medicine in that way, whether I'm doing it or someone else.

Mary Agyapong

I'm the type of person who thinks 'let thy food be thy medicine, and thy medicine be thy food'. I'm very much in tune with what I put in my body, and what effect it has on me.

I have a scepticism around 'Big Pharma' because I'm aware it's a business – in order to keep themselves funded they need people to be unwell. It's a system. That may be something I've internalised from my family. I'm British born Ghanaian, and my parents moved from Ghana to here many years ago. One thing that made it quite difficult was that for me, as a PhD student with an insight into what research is like, I am well aware that Black women like you and I are underrepresented in clinical trials of medicine. So I'm thinking, hold on, there's no guarantee that this will be right for me! I had already not been able to see Black GPs, or Black therapists, so this seemed to be another layer in the issue.

Hormone treatments

One interview focused specifically on the experiences of a friend undergoing hormone treatments. We know that Black people often suffer negative treatment outcomes from doctors and being gender non-conforming negatively impacts that treatment even further. The negative experiences of Black people with doctors often comes as a result of historical and ongoing devaluation of our experiences of pain, and assumptions that we overexaggerate ailments, which leads to issues such as a maternal mortality rate that is five times higher for Black women than white women in the UK,[5] and racist medical textbooks that suggest Black people 'report higher pain intensity than other cultures' and 'believe suffering and pain are inevitable'.[6] This means we often have to become our own doctors, carefully researching our own symptoms, treatment, and relying on the experiences of other Black people.

<u>Anonymous</u>

Recently I was put on progesterone, because I've been taking testosterone for almost a year, I still have my cycle and I was going to try to stop it. I have a lot of concerns, because I already have premenstrual dysphoric disorder (PMDD), which is similar to incredibly intense PMS: it's not very well documented, and it makes you feel really suicidal.

I warned my doctors about it, but they still put me on progesterone which intensified the PMDD. I had to take myself off the medication, and it makes me really dubious about medication and healthcare.

In terms of my journey with hormones, it can feel like there is a lack of care for Black trans people. Looking out for my own medical needs is necessary. I'm thinking I should have done more research into the side effects, but you expect your doctor to know these things and be looking out for you, and know what to put you on and what not to based on your medical history. As a trans person that's not a luxury I have, you have to become your own doctor a lot of the time.

I have a private endocrinologist who does my hormones for me. The NHS has a three-year waiting list for the gender clinic, so I pay around £140 for a 50-minute session every six months at an endocrinologist out in Brighton.

Mental health

By far the most common story here was one related to mental health. Concerns about family opinion were repeated, as well as fears of side-effects of mind-altering medication and also a lack of positive examples among Black people of psych medication improving lives.

<u>Anonymous</u>

Recently I've been reaching out for support regarding my depression, including therapy and medication. I'd never gone to the doctors specifically for mental health issues before, so this was also about me getting a formal diagnosis.

I think my mum was upset by that. From the get-go she's been very anti-medication, but has been supportive in my reaching out for therapy and CBT. I think she's scared that I'll become dependent on it, or that it'll somehow stop me from finishing my third year, as she always talks about medication as if it's a short-term type of thing even when I try to explain that my diagnosis will only worsen if I don't take advantage of all the support offered.

I want to take the medication, but I go home every holiday, and with my living space for next year being unstable, it's very possible I'll be back home where I can't hide that I'm on medication. I'm currently much better, but my low episodes hit hard and suddenly and it's terrifying being in a situation where I can't have something that would help me through those slumps, especially when I think she thinks I'm just 'very stressed'.

I understand where she's coming from, as she has friends who went on antidepressants when she was young, and the medication messed with their health. She doesn't want that for me, and this is all coming from a loving headspace, where she is helping the only way she knows how to. But even then, I know it would cause a massive fight if I went on them and she found out.

The opinion of relatives about treatment was cited more frequently by foreign patients than local patients. This could be due to differences regarding familial cohesion, which can be considered as traditionally stronger in Southern and Eastern countries than in Western Europe or the US. Indeed, migrants included in this study moved from collectivist (or socio-centric) societies to an individualistic (or ego-centric) one. (Thorens et al., 2008, p. 60)

<u>Rianna Davis</u>

When I got officially diagnosed with severe depression and anxiety it was a shock to my family. My mum and grandma were immediately really supportive, and started reading about both diagnoses, but especially depression.

I was already scared about taking antidepressants, I guess as an inherent cultural thing – I don't like taking tablets and was scared about the adjustment period. But my mum and grandma didn't want me to take them because they were worried about me turning into a 'zombie': being able to function but not being myself, or it having a long-lasting effect on my body. So in the end I never took them, and gave them to my friend one day who had run out of her meds.

For medications, concerns were raised about side effects, effectiveness, addiction potential, dependency on medication in order to function, and the length of time needed to complete treatment. (Cooper-Patrick et al., 1997, p. 436)

Mental health is hugely taboo in Jamaican culture, and as I get older I understand that a lot of the family members that were never spoken about probably suffered from severe mental health issues. My mum herself had very severe postnatal depression when she had me – she told me I didn't smile until I was about two, I was a very serious baby.

My mum and grandma were also both nurses within the NHS, and they have an inherent distrust of Western medicine, especially psych medication, because they don't think they have seen it work. They're also both Christian so I had to take some time to explain to them both when I got diagnosed that prayer is great, but I was also going to need more action than just that.

Many patients felt that their usual support systems were ineffective during a depressive episode because of their own discomfort with asking for help, their need to appear strong to family members and friends, and the lack of understanding regarding depression on the part of many family members and friends. (Cooper-Patrick et al., 1997, p. 435)

Iona MacPherson

Stigma was perceived as a particularly important barrier to getting treatment for the Black patients in this study. Many of them felt that the idea of professional help for mental health problems was not culturally acceptable among their family members or peers. (Cooper-Patrick et al., 1997, p. 435-6)

I understand my family's viewpoints on medication. Doctors are very quick to offer drugs when talking or trauma therapy could be more helpful, but for that you'd need an entire upheaval of the NHS, and far more resources. I've also seen my family, and particularly the Black women, put in danger medically time and time again because doctors do not pay enough attention to their symptoms or their accounts of how they feel.

Two years on, I still believe medication can help, but I find myself turning to holistic medication as well. My grandma has always believed bush tea, aloe vera, and a good Jamaican meal can cure anything: she sends me bottles and bottles of sambucol at university to keep me healthy, and even with the coronavirus pandemic she's still scouring Boots for sambucol.

What is your general opinion about taking psychiatric medications? Non-EU responded 28.6% positive as compared to 51.9% positive from Swiss people. (Thorens et al., 2008, p. 58)

Dr. Samara Linton

My mum didn't take it well when I started antidepressants. She was scared, because in her eyes it's one thing to take physical medication, and another to take medication that affects your brain. Every Black person she knows who takes brain-related medication isn't very well, is imprisoned, or institutionalised: there are no positive examples for her, all she has is negative reference points.

I had to convince her, reassure her, I had to become the expert in that situation. Now it's been a few years, and she still doesn't love it. She'd never say 'don't forget your meds', and once I found them in the bin and I swear she did it on purpose! But they've realised it hasn't harmed my life in any way, and that I feel like they are doing good, so they kind of accept that. It's even reached the point where my mum has asked me to give my opinion to a friend thinking of going on similar medication, so we've come a long way.

Religion

The impact of religion in these interviews was mixed – some condemned reliance on the church as leading to exploitation of desperate families in need, citing churches that offered to intensify the amount of prayer they do for your ailments depending on the amount you donate: if you donate £1000 you get to sit at the front of the church, for £500 the row behind and so on, exploiting the fear that doctors neglect Black patients, and providing a financial alternative. Others took comfort from the word and challenged the view of faith as oppositional to healthcare.

Mary Agyapong

I think there's stigma attached to medication, where it's fine to take medication for your body, but less so for your mind. I'm a Christian, as is my family, and faith is one of the cornerstones of my life. Medication isn't a crutch, it's something I personally view as temporary, but often with faith you hear about people praying instead of relying on medication, and thinking medication is in opposition to prayer. I don't see why they are pitted against each other.

We don't think that God doesn't want us to take paracetamol, but for some reason with antidepressants we see it as oppositional to faith, which I don't understand! I found myself looking online, and on blogs, trying to find someone who's Black and Christian and going through the same struggles, but people aren't always super open about it. I was searching for that assurance that it was okay to want to be on medication. My faith hasn't changed, I still get hope and comfort from the word.

> *Black patients cited spirituality as a coping mechanism more frequently than white patients. [Black patients] also discussed using church and church members for support more frequently than [white patients]. (Cooper-Patrick et al., 1997, 435)*

Sexual health

Often hand in hand with religion came reluctant attitudes towards sexual health, and contraception. As far as vaccines, that awareness of Black people's historical role as guinea pigs for medical testing leaves many of us understandably reluctant to participate in medical treatments that are seen as experimental – many Black people I know are already expressing reluctance to use the as yet non-existent COVID-19 vaccine in the future.

Dr. Samara Linton

The only vaccine that I remember not being allowed to have was the HPV vaccine, and I honestly think a lot of it was just the way in which it was explained to parents, and even in my class loads of us didn't have it, because I think it was just seen as the vaccine that you need if you're going to have sex, because HPV is a disease that's sexually transmitted. As far as mum was concerned, 'you ain't having sex, so you don't need this vaccine'!

She felt it was encouraging promiscuity, especially because it was given to us at such a young age. I think the idea that this protects you for your whole life, so even when you get older and get married it protects you, wasn't ever really explained. So my mum didn't let me have it for that reason and because I wasn't having it, some of my friends were like, 'oh, maybe I shouldn't have it either' and they spoke to their parents and their parents wouldn't let them have it. These people don't think about Black families when they say, 'this vaccine is for a sexually transmitted infection', what's wrong with them? There was a lack of cultural competency in the way they advertised it, especially for a vaccine aimed at twelve-year-old girls.

On top of that, we were the first year to get it, and it felt like we were the test generation. And being Black people, with a history of having medical treatments tested on us non-consensually, having the power now to opt out, we took it. Maybe my parents were fine with vaccines that have been around for a while and been tried on lots of people, but to try out a new vaccine on her young child for something that as far as she's concerned I'll never have exposure to, it didn't make sense, and of course I didn't question it.

Black people's wariness of the healthcare system is consistently validated anew, and many of us continue to challenge medical advice we are given, turning to our own experts, our own networks of solidarity and resistance for information that takes our bodies, histories and cultures into account.

I know that my children will have the HPV vaccine, and access to whatever contraceptives, medications, or whatever else they may need. I also know that when they catch colds, I'll be placing a few drops of stinging mentholated shilling oil on their pillows before they sleep, and rubbing Vicks Vaporub on their forehead, nostrils, throat and chest. I'll let them skip the bush tea though.

What next?

- **Black Minds Matter UK** (*blackmindsmatteruk.com*) – Black Minds Matter UK connects Black individuals and families with free professional mental health services across the UK. They aim to make mental health topics relevant and accessible for all Black people in the UK.
- **The Colour of Madness** edited by Rianna Walcott and Dr Samara Linton

Iletz: a locus

reconfiguring my body as a body that will bleed

by Anna Walsh

LAST YEAR, MY 15-year-old sister got the HPV vaccine in school. Many of her year elected not to receive it. When my parents originally mentioned the vaccine to me, they were leaning towards refusing it, based on fears amassing through both parents and student bodies that were rooted in lack of information, and fear of vengeful, irreversible side effects. My sister goes to the school I attended, an all-girls Catholic school, replete during my time with nuns and intolerance. I spoke to my parents, telling them what I had learned only by virtue of not receiving the vaccine: that HPV was not an STD, that it was essentially present in most people, and that stress, smoking, and a weakened immune system puts one much more at risk for HPV developing into something harmful.

My younger sister has stresses of her own, and I do not want to detract from those. But as someone who has, like many, worked in a highly stressful environment, lived in a hostile city, become ill periodically with anxiety and chronic muscle pain, I felt it was important to drive home the importance of stress being a factor. This is not to list the grievances of living, but to acknowledge forces beyond ignorance that compound the issue. Forces like class, sexuality, and gender, and the heavy cloy of shame that sticks in Irish medical history. When I was 15, there was no HPV vaccine available to us in Ireland. There was little sex education, and only the barest belief in us, the students, to do anything besides fuck up. At 17, I was put into one of the top Honours English classes and spent most of those classes in the bathroom or in the town library; upon advising us on our personal essays, our teacher had warned us that anything relating to topics such as unplanned pregnancies would be detrimental to our overall mark, regardless of quality of writing or objectives met.

This is not unusual. Ireland has a long and violent history with reproductive rights, and the rights of a person to live freely. To be a person with a womb was, and still is, a punitive position to hold. The checklist of decriminalisations and repeals are relevant here: homosexuality in 1993, divorce in 1995, marriage equality in 2015, abortion in 2018. Trans healthcare is almost non-existent. Everyone is related to someone with a whispered, pained story of enforced stillbirth, of families wrenched into dutiful existence, of long lines of intergenerational trauma crossing over and back in the forms of mental illness, substance abuse, and suicide. The Church and State worked hard to break its people, and this is still legible in its psychic and physical presence among the Irish people.

In 2016, I received my letter from the Health Service Executive (HSE) informing me that turning 25 entitled me to a free smear test, and I ignored it. I felt sick thinking about what would happen, afraid to be touched anywhere, and deeply distrustful. I had spent the tail end of the last recession working and living in Dublin, grasping and drinking anything that made me feel safe, or numb. In 2016, I was entering deep recovery mode, from both sexual assault and emotional abuse, and could not begin to comprehend taking care of myself in a basic way, let alone willingly placing myself in a doctor's office, to be *seen to*, on such intimate terms. I did not know how to really talk about it, in the way I have not known how to really talk about periods and hormonal issues, because I have never felt comfortable being treated as a woman.

I do not identify with the gender binary in any way, beyond it being a signifier still in use with many people whom I love and respect, and many more I do not. In 2016, this knowledge was buried deeply underneath a lifetime of being forced into a certain way of living, one which I hated, and which caused me to hate myself. I knew only that everything I had experienced could be covered in one easy blanket statement – bad and scary. That touch made me feel sick to my stomach. Being touched in a way that affirmed me as innately *female*, in a way that told me the other party could use this definition to control my bodily rights, and would hold it over the definition I had of myself, was something I struggled to comprehend, or even articulate to myself.

My brain worked overtime to justify avoiding touch. My logic insisted that a smear test would brutalise me in my already sensitive state, and anxiety knotted self-preservation to a dark and churning place, arising only at 2 and 3am with the rhythmic insistence that I was probably dying anyways; that it was probably better not to know. I continued to ignore the letter, continued to panic at night and emerge the next morning having packaged the worry away, convincing myself that I would simply book it the next day, the next week, the next month. I drank on and off. I wrote more and more. My journals and poems circled back to the same things over and over; a desire to be seen differently, a desire to move with confidence. A short piece from 2017 contains the line: 'I want to achieve a // very exact hacking severity // hard edges and twink jeans // & Tilda Swinton hair'.

My will to ignore myself was becoming unsustainable. I could not replenish my energy quick enough to stay on lockdown from my desires. I cut my hair in stages, from ass-length blue/grey to a natural brown bob, offset by a dykey fringe, to then shaving the sides, then the back. I eventually brought a photo of Cillian Murphy into my long-suffering hairdresser, urging him to just go for it. I went on dates with other gays, other trans people.

I also overworked. I had been feeling a heavy pressure in my pelvis and stomach, and obsessive physical inspection led to the discovery of a large, round Bartholin's cyst. Bartholin's cysts are common and usually painless, occurring near the opening of the vagina, from a blocked gland or sometimes stress. Wrecked, I began to take iron and B12 supplements again, and decided not to drink or smoke for a while. I decided to just finally get the smear, to just fucking do it, and signed up with a local GP. A few weeks later, in the doctor's office, the cyst had disappeared, and I recited all of the measures I had implemented as a result of being almost immovably anxious. I spoke to her about knowing I probably just needed therapy but also that I was undeniably in pain most of the time. She sympathised, and said she would send me for blood tests, and that the nurse would perform my smear test. I felt in control of myself, and told myself I was being brave, that I should not punish myself for having a body by letting it become sick with preventable illnesses.

The smear itself was okay. I kept thinking, it's just uncomfortable, not painful. I had read and heard this from many people, as if discomfort in a vulnerable place is removed entirely from pain. The way I thought of it was like getting my tongue pierced: weird, not immediately painful in a stabbing way, but certainly not something I was happy to experience. The nurse was pragmatic and thoughtful, apologising for the cold metal of the speculum. She told me to take deep breaths as she wound it in and said I would get my results in a month or so, that there was a huge backlog of tests being done at the moment. This was in March 2018. I felt okay, and some pride that I did not feel humiliated, or irreparably crushed.

In 2018, the Cervical Check scandal was ongoing in Ireland, resulting in 206 women developing cervical cancer after misdiagnosed smear checks assuring them there were no abnormalities. I muted the words 'cervix' and 'cervical' and 'scandal' on Twitter, and received a letter informing me of the presence of bacterial vaginosis as well as irregular cells in my cervix. I was prescribed antibiotics and assigned a date for a colposcopy and biopsy to examine the cells further. The colposcopy procedure was developed by doctors experimenting on Jewish inmates in Auschwitz, primarily by Eduard Wirths and H Hinselmann. The racist, brutal history of gynaecology is not a secret, the speculum famously pioneered by James Marion Sims, who experimented on enslaved African American women and children, performing some 30 operations without anaesthetic on one woman, Anarcha Westcott.

When I went in for my colposcopy, the doctor remarked how sorry she was that my first experience of a smear test had been a negative result. She implored me to stop smoking, telling me about her own trials with quitting. She explained that they were going to apply a gel to numb the area for biopsy, and that it would make my heart beat faster than usual. Another doctor was present for the procedure, standing beside me as the other inserted the gel. The anaesthetic shot up to my chest and my whole body vibrated. I started to cry. They both encouraged me, assuring me it was normal, the emotions were bound to be overwhelming. One of them held my hand as I cried, and told me I was good, that it was going to be fine. They inserted the scope and after a few minutes of probing, had to do it again in order to get a usable sample. I nodded and gritted myself, trying to relax enough to allow insertion, trying not to vomit. They asked me if I had anyone waiting for me, and when I said no, they urged me to curl up with painkillers and chocolate for the evening. They kept reassuring me that the pressure would last only for a moment, for a few minutes. They communicated with each other in a quiet, moving symmetry of suggestions and agreements, one pushing and extracting, the other observing. It was clear they worked well together.

After this, I was told to take pads with me, and to take it easy. I was not to have intercourse, take baths or use tampons for at least a month. I was in pain for weeks afterwards, feeling fragile and weary, a little grossed out by the remnants of the anaesthetic that came out in what looked like pieces of black crumb. I received a letter saying there had been precancerous cells detected, that they would be removed by LLETZ procedure, and advised me to bring someone to the hospital with me if possible.

I got on the Luas in Dublin at 7:30am, in the dark autumn morning. I sat in the waiting room with my mother, unable to log into the Wi-Fi, staring at magazines about cancer and new babies. I just wanted to get the letter saying I didn't need to come back, that I was okay for another year. I was mostly concerned at that point with how long the recovery process was, that I would be another six weeks fucked up, as well as unable to have sex. Once called in, the doctor explained again to me what was involved in the procedure. I nodded, not really listening, trying to remain calm in order to just get through it.

I was asked to change into a gown and lay back on the long chair. I tried not to clench my entire body. I tried to breathe deeply as I once again opened my legs and prepared for insertion, for undeniable pressure and the feeling of something moving inside of me. I went home to nurse my cramps.

A few days after, on Saturday night, Pillow Queens were playing in town, a hot lesbian band from Dublin. I sat in my room in Ranelagh, crying and checking how much I bled every 20 minutes. I had rung Holles Street earlier, a nurse telling me in a practised, kind voice to keep taking painkillers and to rest if I could, that the bleeding should ease off in a day or so. I was bleeding so much I had given up on using pads, using toilet paper instead to soak the majority of what was coming. Small pieces of the silver nitrate they had used to cauterise my cervix came through too, interspersing with black and red clots. To speak about the pain I was feeling seems almost insignificant, when my memory of that weekend is almost solely one of pure and totalising fear. I felt as though I were being hysterical, muscle memories of self-directed shame overtaking my nervous system. I left my bed only to go to the bathroom.

The bleeding slowed over the weekend, and my girlfriend came over to make me soup. Dosed in painkillers, I watched *The Princess Bride* for the first time, afraid that if I moved too abruptly the bleeding would begin again. I read forum after forum of people panicking, listing the procedures they had had and how confused they were about the aftercare, or if they had infections, or were haemorrhaging. Weeks passed and I was still in pain, the first period I had after it close to unbearable.

As I write this, I am on my period. It has changed in the past two years, from quite regular, sore-but-not-awful, to more haphazard, looser in its punctuality. It starts, stops for a day, then returns with a vengeance the next. It wakes me in the night, a heavy rock in my stomach, as I sweat and toss and turn to find a position that gives me relief. I now have to take painkillers for almost its entirety, which beforehand I staunchly refused unless the pain was debilitating.

After the LLETZ, the doctor remarked that it could make it more difficult for me to conceive. I am less in control of my PMS and feel less in control of my body in general. It is strange because I am more rooted now in my sense of wellbeing, my age, and sense of identity, but sometimes it feels as though it is at the cost of losing days and nights to my hormones, becoming more embodied in myself, at the behest of that which I put so much energy into ignoring.

What next?

- ***Medical Bondage: Race, Gender, and the Origins of American Gynecology*** by Deirdre Cooper Owens

endnotes
and references

No Country for Neurodivergent Women

Andrews, Julie. 'I Have Confidence'. The Sound of Music, 1965. *Spotify*.

Baker, Evadine et al. 'Maria'. The Sound of Music, 1965. *Spotify*.

Constitution of Ireland. 1937. Irish Statute Book.

Maté, Gabór. *Scattered Minds: The Origins and Healing of Attention Deficit Disorder*. London: Vermillon, 2019.

'The One with the Secret Closet'. 2002. Friends: The Complete Eighth Season, Writ. David Crane, Marta Kauffman, Brian Buckner and Sebastian Jones, dir. Kevin Bright,Warner Brothers, .

Mrs Doubtfire. 1993. Perf. Robin Williams and Sally Field, dir. Chris Columbus. Twentieth Century Fox, .

Solden, Sari. 2005. *Women with Attention Deficit Disorder: Embrace Your Differences and Transform Your Life*. CA: Underwood books.

The Sound of Music. 1965. Perf. Julie Andrews, dir. Robert Wise. Twentieth Century Fox.

Getting Off the Back Foot with Male Fertility Health

1. NHS Infertility. Available at: https://www.nhs.uk/conditions/infertility/

2. Tommy's Pregnancy Hub. Available at: https://www.tommys.org/pregnancy-information/impregnant/early-pregnancy/how-common-miscarriage

3. Azura Vascular Care. Available at: https://www.azuravascularcare.com/infovaricocele/male-infertility-statistics/

4. Shmerling, R. and Shmerling, A. 2018. 'Fertility and Diet: Is there a connection?' Harvard Health Blog. Available at:

https://www.health.harvard.edu/blog/fertility-and-diet-isthere-a-connection-2018053113949

5. NCBI. 2012. Available at: https://www.ncbi.nlm.nih.gov/pmc/articlesPMC3605892/

6. Gani, A. 2015. 'More babies born to women 35 or older than under 25 for first time'. *The Guardian*. Available at: https://www.theguardian.com/lifeandstyle/2015/nov/16/more-babies-born-to-women-35-older-than-under-25--england-and-wales

7. Deatsman, S., Vasilopoulos, T., and Rhoton-Viasak, A. 2016. 'Age and Fertility: A Study on Patient Awareness'. *JBRA Assisted Reproduction*. 20(3). p. 99–106.

8. Christie, T. 2018. 'Causes of male infertility' *Parla Blog* Available at: https://www.myparla.com/causes-of-male-infertility/

9. Agarwal, A., Virk, G., Ong, C., and S du Plessis, S. 2014. *The World Journal of Men's Health*. 32(1). p. 1-17.

10. Carlsen, M. H., Halvorsen, L. B., Blomhoff, R., 'Antioxidants in Nuts and Seeds'. Chapter Six. In Preedy, V.R., Watson, R.R. & Patel, V.B. 2011, Nuts & seeds in health and disease prevention, 1st edn, Academic Press, London; Brlington, MA.

The Self-Made Body

1. Nutt, D. J., King, L. A., and Philips, L. D. 2010. 'Drug harms in the UK: a multicriteria decision analysis'. *Lancet* 376. p. 1558–1565.

Notes from a Medical Menopause

1. Online Etymology Dictionary.

2. Brogan, K. and Loberg, K. 2016. *A Mind of your own: the truth about depression and how women can heal their bodies to reclaim their lives*. Harper Wave.

'Man…I Feel Like a Woman'

1. Jones, Z. 2013. 'That was dysphoria? 8 signs and symptoms of indirect gender dysphoria' *Gender Analysis*. Available at: https://genderanalysis.net/articles/that-was-dysphoria-8-signs-and-symptoms-of-indirect-gender-dysphoria/

Don't Tell Me to Calm Down

1. Showalter, E. 1987. *The Female Malady: Women, Madness and English Culture,*

1930–1980. [2014 Reprint]. Virago Press.

2. Gilman, C. P. 1981. *The Yellow Wallpaper.* London: Virago Press.

3. Seyle, H. 1978. *The Stress of Life.* [Revised edition]. McGraw Hill/Schaum's Outlines.

4. Gleason, S. 2018. 'This is how your stree turns into sickness'. *Furturity.* Available at: https://www.futurity.org/stress-sickness-1651672/

5. 'Misdiagnoses of heart attacks in women' *British Heart Foundation.* Available at: https://www.bhf.org.uk/informationsupport/heart-matters-magazine/medical/women/misdiagnosis-of-heart-attacks-in-women

6. Tunks, E., Bellissimo, A., & Roy, R. (Eds.). *Chronic pain: Psychosocial factors in rehabilitation (2ⁿᵈ ed.)* Robert E Krieger Publishing Co, 1990.

7. Autoimmune Diseases in Women. 2002. American Autoimmune and Related Diseases Association, Inc. *Women and autoimmunity*, https://www.aarda.org/who-we-help/patients/women-and-autoimmunity/

Darwin, C. 1871. *The Descent of Man.* [1981 Reprint]. Princeton, N.J.: Princeton University Press.

Spencer, H. 1876. *The Principles of Sociology (Volume 1).* [2004 Reprint]. University Press of the Pacific.

Maudsley, H. 1873. *Body and Mind.* London: Macmillan.

Telling Hormonal Stories

1. Quotes throughout are either from conversations that took place in the course of academic research, including interviews and participant observation, or from textual documents that were analysed for the purpose of academic research, including news and public media articles and archival documents. Interviewees gave permission for their quotes to be used (anonymised) in publications, and all textual documents analysed were in the public domain. All names are pseudonymous.

2. Sport governing bodies like the International Olympic Committee (IOC) and World Athletics have eligibility regulations for women's sports that impose a threshold on how much testosterone some women athletes can have in their bodies to be eligible to compete. See Jordan-Young, Rebecca and Karkazis, Katrina (2019), *Testosterone: An Unauthorised Biography.* Cambridge and London: Harvard University Press; and Erikainen, Sonja (2020), *Gender Verification and the Making of the Female Body in Sport: A History of the Present.* London: Routledge

3. This is called 'therapeutic exemption'. The World Anti-Doping Agency (WADA) can grant this exemption to men who can demonstrate that they require testosterone supplementation for 'medical reasons'. See Erikainen, Sonja 2020, *Gender Verification and the Making of the Female Body in Sport: A History of the Present*. London: Routledge

4. Granzow, K. 2007. 'Deconstructing "Choice": The Social Imperative and Women's Use of the Birth Control Pill'. *Culture, Health & Sexuality* 9(1). p. 43–54.

5. Preciado, P. B. 2013. *Testo Junkie: Sex, Drugs, and Biopolitics in the Pharmacopornographic Era*. (See for instance pages 28, 167–168, 205–207 and 230).

6. Gunn, J. and Mary, D. V. 2010. 'Regulation through postfeminist pharmacy. Promotional discourse and menstruation' in *Governing the Female Body: Gender, Health and Networks of Power*, ed. Reed, Lori and Saukko, Paula, p. 121.

7. See Bergland, C. 2013. 'Cortisol: Why the "stress hormone" is public enemy no. 1'. *Psychology Today.* Available at: https://www.psychologytoday.com/us/blog/the-athletes-way/201301/cortisol-why-the-stress-hormone-is-public-enemy-no-1.

8. See Cardoso, C., Ellenbogen, M., Serravalle, L., and Linnen, A. 2013. 'Stress-Induced Negative Mood Moderates the Relation Between Oxytocin Administration and Trust: Evidence for the Tend-and-befriend Response to Stress.' *Psychoneuroendocrinology* 38(11). p. 2800–2804.

9. See Szabo, S, Tache, Y., and Somogyi, A. 2012. 'The Legacy of Hans Selye and the origins of stress research: A retrospective 75 Years after his landmark brief 'letter' to the editor of nature'. *Stress* 15(5). p. 472–478.

Blood Is Back

1. 'Plan International UK's Research On Period Poverty and Stigma'. 2013. *Plan International.* Available at: https://plan-uk.org/media-centre/plan-international-uks-research-on-period-poverty-and-stigma

2. 'Without expression; Silencencing the role of the menstraul cycle in ill health – part 2'. 2016, November 29. *Menstrual Matters.* Available at: https://www.menstrual-matters.com/blog/without-expression-part-2/

3. Pasha-Robinson, L. 2017, March 20. 'Nearly half of girls do not know what is happening when they start their first period, study reveals'. *The Independent.* Available at: https://www.independent.co.uk/life-style/health-and-families/health-news/girls-teenagers-start-period-menstruation-

An Impersonal History of Self-Medication

1. I can't remember exactly where I read about her, but I imagine it is the same case mentioned by Dean Spade in his article 'Mutilating Gender'.

2. The wait times vary across the UK, because there is more than one clinic serving trans people in the UK. In Ireland there is only one such clinic. When you consider that these clinics frequently require trans people to undergo psychiatric evaluation before even being added to waiting lists for *attendance* at the clinic itself, and that these evaluations have their own waiting lists, it is possible for a trans person to spend as many as six years going from coming out to getting their first prescription (this does not take into account that many give up or are discouraged, and may have to delay or even restart the entire process).

3. By safe here I mean *secu*re. Information on how to access hormone therapy must remain in the hands of the community and not be widely accessible to the general public.

4. Depending on the kind of hormone therapy (pill, patch, injectable, or gel) the cost varies. The low end of that scale is about 100–120 euro per person per year, the high end 400 euro +.

5. Naturally, the end goal is for healthcare access to be free – one tactic, however, the LGBT community must adopt is to foster and protect self-medicating communities, and to make use of their knowledge and expertise.

6. See Duncan's 1944 essay 'The Homosexual in Society', Milk's 1978 'Hope Speech', and Kramer's 1983 essay '1,112 and Counting'.

7. See 'Toward a Gay Theory for the 80s' in *Bruce Boone Dismembered*, Nightboat Books, 2020.

8. *Come Out!* was the first Gay Liberation magazine, and can be found at http://outhistory.org/exhibits/show/come-out-magazine-1969-1972/the-come-out-archive

6. Conflict within the Gay Liberation movement – Gay Lib, especially in New York, was markedly diverse in its first years – over transgender people and trans healthcare was present from the beginning. Gay Lib offshoots like STAR (Street Transvestite Action Revolutionaries) and QLF (Queens Liberation Front) demanded free, immediate access to hormone therapy, surgery, and legal gender recognition for all people – other organisations, like the Red Butterfly, opposed *any* such access. Arguably this came to a head in

1973 when lesbian groups issued death threats to a transsexual lesbian Beth Elliott and drove her from the lesbian community, and attacked (rhetorically) drag queens, transvestites, and transgender people at the Christopher Street Liberation Day March (both Sylvia Rivera and Lee Brewster spoke out against them). It is well known that, as a rule, Dennis Altman can not write a book about gay politics *or his life apparently* without passing several condescending remarks about trans people. If you are trans and interested in this history, check out the Small Trans Library (branches in Dublin and Glasgow), where I run on-and-off-again workshops on the Gay Liberation movement.

I'm Wearing Docs, Michael

1.   Didion, Joan. 1968. *Slouching Towards Bethlehem*. Farrar, Straus, and Giroux.

Clot

1.   'RDA Drug Safety Communication: Updated information about the risk of blood clots in women taking birth control pills containing drospirenone'. 2012. April 10. *United States Food & Drug Adminstration*. Available at: https://www.fda.gov/drugs/drug-safety-and-availability/fda-drug-safety-communication-updated-information-about-risk-blood-clots-women-taking-birth-control

2.   Toufexis, A. 2017, July 27. 'Medicine: Coping with Eve's Curse'. *Time Magazine*. Available at: http://content.time.com/time/magazine/article/0,9171,949233,00.html

Mood Swings and Misunderstandings

1.   Grigg-Spall, H. 2016. 'The pill is linked to depression – and doctors can no longer ignore it'. *The Guardian*.

2.   Skovlund, C. W., Mørch, L. S., Kessing, L. V., & Lidegaard, Ø. 2016. Association of hormonal contraception with depression. *JAMA Psychiatry*, 73(11), 1154–1162.

3.   Almendrala, A. 2016. 'Landmark Study Links Hormonal Birth Control And Depression'. *Huffington Post*.

Period, the End

1.   Cambridge Dictionary [Online] 'Oestrogen'. Available at: https://dictionary.cambridge.org/dictionary/english/oestrogen

2.   *Robinson, M. N. 1959. The Power of Sexual Surrender. [Republished 2017] Phocion Books.*

3.	'Period Pain' *UK National Health Service*. Available at: https://www.nhs.uk/conditions/period-pain/

4.	*Our Bodies, Ourselves*, by Boston Women's Health Collective, 1971. UK edition edited by Angela Phillips and Jill Rakus. Republished by Simon & Schuster, 2011. Last updated online, 2018.

5.	'Period Pain' *UK National Health Service*. Available at: https://www.nhs.uk/conditions/period-pain/

6.	Gurevich, R. 2020, April 20. '6 Signs your period cramps are not normal'. *Very WellFamily*. Available at: https://www.verywellfamily.com/signs-your-period-cramps-are-not-normal-1959947

7.	'Menstraul Cycle: Dealing with Cramps'. 2019. November 7. *Cigna International*. Available at: https://www.cigna.com/individuals-families/health-wellness/hw/medical-topics/menstrual-cycle-aq0001

8.	Benton, E. 2019, May 22. 'The 1 surprising reason you may need to drink more water, according to a doctor'. *Popsugar*. Available at: https://www.popsugar.co.uk/fitness/Should-I-Drink-More-Water-My-Period-46192697

9.	Thornton, E. 2019, January 17. 'Can cinnamon help period cramps?'. *A. Vogel*. Available at: https://www.avogel.co.uk/health/periods/can-cinnamon-help-period-cramps/

10.	Leonard, J. 2020, January 15. 'Depression during period: Everything you need to know'. *Medical News Today*. Available at: https://www.medicalnewstoday.com/articles/327490#why-hormones-affect-mood

11.	'Period pains: Can anti-inflammatory drugs help?'. 2007, November 16. *NCBI*. Available at: https://www.ncbi.nlm.nih.gov/books/NBK279323/#:~:text=Anti%2Dinflammatory%20painkillers%20are%20often,period%20pain%20in%20that%20way.

12.	Smith, R. P. and Ellis, J. 2002. 'NSAIDs: Is newer better for dysmenorrhea?'. *OBG Management*. 14(7). p. 71–81. *Ibid*.

13.	Scott, K. 2016, May 25. '#MenstruationMatters: Taboo around menstruation causing women shame, researcher says'. *ABC News*. Available at: https://www.abc.net.au/news/2016-05-25/taboo-around-menstruation-causing-women-shame/744537

14..	'Period shame, misinformation linked to serious human rights concerns'. 2018, June 7. *United Nations Population Fund*. Available at: https://www.unfpa.org/news/period-shame-misinformation-linked-serious-human-rights-concerns

15. Druet, A. 2017, September 8. 'How did menstruation become taboo?'. *Clue*. Available at: https://helloclue.com/articles/culture/how-did-menstruation-become-taboo

Blood and Bone

1. Camacho, P. M. 2017, May, 5. 'Osteoporosis Causes'. *Endocrine Web*. Available at: https://www.endocrineweb.com/conditions/osteoporosis/osteoporosis-causes
2. Hoffman, M. 2009, April 27. 'Bone scans and bone health screenings'. *WebMD*. Available at: https://www.webmd.com/osteoporosis/features/tests#1
3. National Osteoporosis Foundation. 'General Facts'. Available at: https://www.nof.org/preventing-fractures/general-facts/what-women-need-to-know/

What a Difference a Day Makes

1. UK National Health Service. 'Symptoms: Menopause'. Availabe at: https://www.nhs.uk/conditions/menopause/symptoms/
2. UK Society for Endocrinology.'You and Your Hormones'. Available at: https://www.yourhormones.info/glands/ovaries/
3. Morgan, R. 1982. *The Anatomy of Freedom*, p50.
4. Manguso, S. 2019, June 17. 'Where are all the books about menopause?'. *The New Yorker*. Available at: https://www.newyorker.com/magazine/2019/06/24/where-are-all-the-books-about-menopause.

Change: The Bitter Pill Medicine Must Continue to Swallow

1. Farquhar, M. 2018, January 27. 'Number of women entering medical school rises after decade of decline'. *BMJ Journal*. [360:K202]. Available at: https://www.bmj.com/bmj/section-pdf/959692?path=/bmj/360/8138/Careers.full.pdf
2. Kline, R. 2014. 'The "snowy white peaks" of the NHS: a survey of discrimination in governance and leadership and the potential impact on patient care in London and England'. *Middlesex University Research Repository*. Available at: https://www.england.nhs.uk/wp-content/uploads/2014/08/edc7-0514.pdf
3. Laqueur, T. W. 1992. *Making sex: Body and gender from the Greeks to Freud*. Cambridge, MA: Harvard University Press.

4. World Health Organisation. 2020, January 3. 'Female genital mutilation'. Available at: https://www.who.int/news-room/fact-sheets/detail/female-genital-mutilation

5. King, H. 2015. 'The rise and fall of FGM in Victorian London' *The Conversation*. Available at: https://theconversation.com/the-rise-and-fall-of-fgm-in-victorian-london-38327

6. Rodriguez, S. B. 2018. *Female Circumcision and Clitoridectomy in the United States: A history of a medical treatment*. Cambridge University Press.

7. Parkinson, J. 2016, January 7. 'The significance of Sarah Baartman'. *BBC News Magazine*. Available at: https://www.bbc.co.uk/news/magazine-35240987

8. Birbaumer, N. and Flor, H. 1998. 'Psychobiology'. *Comprehensive Clinical Psychology*. [Volume 1] p. 115–172.

9. Al-Hendy, A., Meyers, E. R., and Stewart, E. 2017. 'Uterine Fibroids: Burden and unmet medical need'. *Seminars in Reproductive Medicine*. 35(6). p. 473–480.

10. National Institute for Health and Care Excellence. 2017, February 9. 'Menopause'. Available at: https://www.nice.org.uk/guidance/qs143/chapter/About-this-quality-standard

11. British Menopause Society. 2017. *Management of the Menopause*. [Sixth Edition].

12. Ozuzu-Nwaiwu, J. 2007, January 10. 'Black women's perceptions of menopause and the use of hormone replacement therapy'. *Nursing Times*. Available at: https://www.nursingtimes.net/clinical-archive/womens-health/black-womens-perceptions-of-menopause-and-the-use-of-hormone-replacement-therapy-10-01-2007/

13. Mitchell, M. and Howarth, C. 2009. 'Trans research review'. *Equality and Human Rights Commission*. [Research Report 27] Available at: https://www.equalityhumanrights.com/sites/default/files/research_report_27_trans_research_review.pdf

If Rabbits, Why Not Women?

1. Margulies, L. 1975. 'History of intrauterine devices', *Bulletin of the New York Academy of Medicine*, Volume 51, p. 662.

2. Junod, S. W. 2007. 'Women over 35 Who Smoke: A Case Study in Risk Management and Risk Communications, 1960–1989', in A. Tone and E. Siegel Watkins (eds.), *Medicating Modern America: Prescription Drugs in History,*

NYU Press, p. 97.

3. Ibid. p. 99.

4. Greene, J. A. Condrau, F., and Watkins, E. S. 2016. *Therapeutic Revolutions: Pharmaceuticals and Social Change in the Twentieth Century*, University Press Scholarship Online, p. 3.

5. Eig, J. 2014. *The Birth of the Pill: How Four Crusaders Reinvented Sex and Launched a Revolution*, W. W. Norton & Company.

6. Watkins, E. S. 2016. 'Reconceiving the Pill: From Revolutionary Therapeutic to Lifestyle Drug', in J. A. Greene, F. Condrau, and E. Siegel Watkins (eds.), *Therapeutic Revolutions: Pharmaceuticals and Social Change in the Twentieth Century*, University Press Scholarship Online, p. 41.

7. Gladwell, M. 2000, March 13. 'John Rock's Error', *The New Yorker*. Available at: https://www.newyorker.com/magazine/2000/03/13/john-rocks-error

8. Pearson, D. and Anderson, J. 1969, March 19. 'FDA Lags on Data for Pill Fatalities', *The Washington Post*.

9. Seaman, B. 1969. *The Doctors' Case Against the Pill*, New York, P.H. Wyden.

10. Turner, C. 2015. 'The Birth of the Pill by Jonathan Eig review – sex, drugs and population control', *The Guardian*. Available at: www.theguardian.com/books/2015/mar/18/the-birth-of-the-pill-jonathan-eig-review-sex-drugs-population-control.

11. Davis, H. 1972. 'Intrauterine contraceptive devices: Present status and future prospects', *American Journal of Obstetrics and Gynecology*, 114(1). p. 134.

12. *Dalkon Shield Recall Commercial, A.H. Robins, 1984*, [online video], Hugo Faces, 20 April 2015, <www.youtube.com/watch?v=AEtbYpvBgCc> [accessed 11 June 2020].

13. Seear, K. 2014. *The Makings of a Modern Epidemic: Endometriosis, Gender and Politics*, Ashgate, p. 128.

Three Magic Days

1. Nummenmaa, L., Glerean, E., Hari, R., and Hietanen, J. K. 2013. 'Bodily map of emotions' *Proceedings of the National Academy of Sciences of the United States of America*. Available at: https://www.pnas.org/content/early/2013/12/26/1321664111.abstract

2. Aquinas, T. 1999. *A Commentary on Aristotle's 'De anima,'* (trans. Robert Pasnau). New Haven, Connecticut.

3. Cohen-Hanegbi, N. 2016. 'A Moving Soul: Emotions in Late Medieval

Medicine'. *Osiris*, vol. 31, no. 1, p. 46–66.

4.   Dean-Jones, L. (1989). 'Menstrual Bleeding according to the Hippocratics and Aristotle'. *Transactions of the American Philological Association (1974–)*, *119, 177.* doi:10.2307/284268, p. 191.

Banana-Leaf Poultices

1.   Here I refer to the example of Dr. Marion Sims, a nineteenth-century physician who is credited as the 'father of modern gynaecology' and conducted experiments on enslaved Black women without anaesthesia, and the infamous 'Tuskegee Study', where 600 African American men were infected with syphilis without their knowledge or consent, in order to observe the results of untreated syphilis.

2.   Here I refer to regimes of forced sterilisation as a means of controlling Black populations via eugenics in American states. https://www.pbs. org/independentlens/blog/unwanted-sterilization-and-eugenics-pro-grams-in-the-united-states/

3.   Research by the Mental Health Foundation indicates that detention rates under the Mental Health Act were four times higher for Black people than white people in the UK. https://www.mentalhealth.org.uk/a-to-z/b/black-asian-and-minority-ethnic-bame-communities

4.   The Office of National Statistics found that Black people in the UK are more than four times more likely to die from Covid-19. https://www. theguardian.com/world/2020/may/07/black-people-four-times-more-likely-to-die-from-covid-19-ons-finds

5.   From BBC article 'Why are black mothers at more risk of dying?' https:// www.bbc.co.uk/news/blogs-trending-41692593

6.   From BBC on the Pearson Medical textbook https://www.bbc.co.uk/ news/blogs-trending-41692593

Cooper-Patrick, L., Powe, N., Jenckes, M., Gonzales, J., Levine, D. and Ford, D., 1997. 'Identification of Patient Attitudes and Preferences Regarding Treatment of Depression'. *Journal of General Internal Medicine*, 12, pp. 431–438.

Thorens, G., Gex-Fabry, M., Zullino, D. and Eytan, A., 2008. 'Attitudes Toward Psychopharmacology Among Hospitalised Patients from Diverse Ethno-cultural Backgrounds'. *BMC Psychiatry*, [online] 8 (55). Available at: https://www.ncbi.nlm.nih.gov/pmc/articles/PMC2478676/ [accessed 27/05/20].

special thanks

So Hormonal was made possible thanks to 330 donors on Kickstarter. We extend a massive thank you to each and every person who donated to this campaign, especially since it coincided with such a strange time of worldwide upheaval. We especially wanted to thank some standout folk below. We couldn't have done this without your time and kindness. Thank you!

Beth Brown

Category Is Books

Connor Grant Divers

Cordelia Sampson

Ely Percy Calderwood

Kathy Garthoff

Gerry Desmond

Gillian Morrissey

Ruthie Johnson

Brooke

Declan Horgan

Mama Hudson

Greg and Wendy Reed

Anonymous

Anne Marie Horgan

Hanah De Laurell

Séamus Murphy

Vincent O'Brien

Lewis

Ceris Jones

Abigail Melton

Lilith Cooper

The Nautilus Bookshop

Gay's the Word Bookshop

Mairi Christine Oliver

Lighthouse Books

Golden Hare Books

Typewronger Books

Housmans Books

Portobello Bookshop

Monstrous
Regiment

@MonstrousRgmt
monstrous-regiment.com